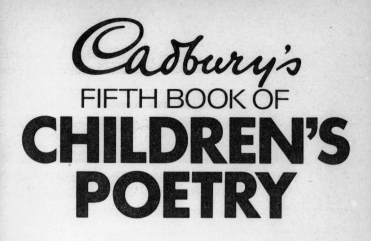

Cadbury's
FIFTH BOOK OF
CHILDREN'S POETRY

A Beaver Book
Published by Arrow Books Limited
62-5 Chandos Place, London WC2N 4NW
An imprint of Century Hutchinson Ltd

London Melbourne Sydney Auckland
Johannesburg and agencies throughout the world

First published 1987
© Cadbury Ltd 1987

Set in Souvenir Light by
JH Graphics Limited, Reading

Made and printed in Great Britain
by Cox & Wyman Ltd
Reading, Berks

ISBN 0 09 951330 7

Contents

Publisher's note

The poems in this book were chosen by a panel of judges which included poets, teachers and educationalists, from nearly 20,000 entries for the Cadbury's National Exhibition of Children's Art 1987/8. This year is the fifth in which there has been a poetry section and the judges – Joan Freeman, educational psychologist and author; Vernon Scannel, poet; Jennifer Curry, anthologist and author; and Kit Wright, poet – were delighted at the great variety of material. They chose as outstanding the work of Jesse Witcome and Christopher Jones, whose poems appear on pages 71 and 152, and 100, 168 and 202 respectively.

Jesse Witcombe lives in London and is fourteen years old. She plans to go to university when she has finished school, possibly to study architecture. As well as her interest in buildings, she also likes rowing, going to the cinema, tennis, swimming and is a keen snooker fan.

Seventeen-year-old Christopher Jones currently lives in Loughborough, and is due to finish school this summer. He plans to go to Newcastle University in the Autumn to continue his literary studies. As well as writing poetry in his spare time, he also enjoys football and basketball.

The judges also highly commended 17 children whose poems appear on pages 11, 12, 25, 31, 56, 65, 74, 76, 104, 122, 146, 164, 196, 198, 200, 201, and 210.

The poems have been arranged under subjects which gives the reader the opportunity to compare the ideas of children from as young as six to mature seventeen year olds. All the illustrations are taken from entries to the Art and Craft section of this year's Exhibition, and they complement the poems in an unusual and satisfying way.

We are very happy to be publishing such an interesting and original book and would like to thank all the writers and artists for their superb efforts. Don't forget, there's another chance to see your poem in print in the Sixth Cadbury's Book of Poetry to be published in 1988. For details on how to enter next year's competition please turn to page 218.

Foreword

This is now the fifth year we have included a Poetry Section within the National Exhibition of Children's Art and we are once again delighted to publish this selection of children's poems.

Choosing these poems from the many thousands of entries submitted was a hard but enjoyable task for our eminent judges, and we sincerely thank them and the young poets themselves. The variety of subject matter and form provides hours of entertaining reading and one cannot help but be inspired by the vivid imagination and understanding of these young people.

It is a pleasure to wander through the pages of this popular book and particularly pleasing for us at Cadbury to be associated with this project. As with previous editions, royalties from Cadbury's Fifth Book of Children's Poetry will be donated to the Save the Children Fund.

Adrian Cadbury

N.B. You can visit the Cadbury's National Exhibition of Children's Art at centres throughout the country. (See page 8 for details of when it will be in your area.)

Cadbury's Fifth Book of Children's Poetry

AWARD WINNERS – Poetry Section
40th National Exhibition of Children's Art 1987/88

1987 ITALIAN TOUR AWARD
Jesse Witcombe (14)
London
Christopher Jones (17)
De Lisle R.C. School, Loughborough

SCHOOL POETRY AWARD
Debenham High School, Stowmarket, Suffolk

ARTHUR LINES POETRY AWARD
Arnold Hunt (17) Hendon, London

HIGHLY COMMENDED
7 and under
Victoria Douglas (7) Lynsted and Norton C.P. School, Sittingbourne, Kent
Lucy Howard (7) New Malden, Surrey
Ernest Ogbonnaya (7) Turnham Junior School, Brockley, London

8-11
Sara-Louise Holland (11) Whittlesford, Cambs

12-14
Aston Hart (14) Debenham High School, Stowmarket, Suffolk
James McLaggan (13) Dulwich College Prep. School, Cranbrook, Kent
P. Walton (12) The Junior School, St Lawrence College, Ramsgate, Kent

15-17
Andrew Campell (16) Newton Mearns, Glasgow, Scotland
Arnold Hunt (17) Hendon, London
Rachel Ind (17) Dursley, Glos
Ruth Leader (16) Westbourne School for Girls, Glasgow, Scotland
Stephen Lee (17) The Aelfgar Centre, Rugeley, Staffs
Sarah Ratheram (15) Harborne, Birmingham
Jason Rutter (17) Ashton Under Lyne Sixth Form College, Lancs
Yen-Yen Teh (15) London
Timothy Troughton (17) Holywood, County Down, Northern Ireland
Helen Wightman (16) Convent of Our Lady of Providence, Alton, Hants

40th Exhibition Tour 1987–1988

LONDON — Westminster Central Hall
Storey's Gate, London SW1H 9NU   Tel: 01-222 8010
Tuesday 17 November 1987–Saturday 28 November 1987
Monday to Saturday 10 a.m. to 10 p.m. Closed Sundays
Saturday 28 November 10 a.m. to 6 p.m.

LINCOLN — The City School
Skellingthorpe Road, Lincoln LN6 0EP   Tel: 0522-683664
Friday 4 December 1987–Saturday 9 January 1988
Monday to Friday 10 a.m. to 12 noon and 1.30 p.m. to 4 p.m.
Saturday and Sunday 10 a.m. to 4 p.m.
Closed 25, 26, 27 and 31 December 1987 and 1 January 1988

BIRMINGHAM — Birmingham Museum & Art Gallery
Chamberlain Square, Birmingham B3 3DH   Tel: 021-235 2834
Friday 15 January 1988–Friday 19 February 1988
Monday to Saturday 9.30 a.m. to 5 p.m.
Sunday 2 p.m. to 5 p.m.

NORWICH — Castle Museum
Castle Meadow, Norwich   Tel: 0603-611277
Saturday 27 February 1988–Sunday 3 April 1988
Monday to Saturday 10 a.m. to 5 p.m.
Sunday 2 p.m. to 5 p.m.

PAISLEY — Museum & Art Galleries
High Street, Paisley, Renfrewshire   Tel: 041-889 3151
Friday 15 April 1988–Friday 13 May 1988
Monday to Saturday 10 a.m. to 5 p.m. Closed Sundays

TORQUAY — Torre Abbey
The Kings Drive, Torquay, Devon TQ2 5JX   Tel: 0803-23593
Friday 20 May 1988–Sunday 11 June 1988
Open 7 days 10 a.m. to 5 p.m.

DURHAM — DLI Museum & Arts Centre
Aykley Heads, Durham DH1 5TU   Tel: 091-384 2214
Friday 17 June 1988–Sunday 17 July 1988
Tuesday to Saturday 10 a.m. to 5 p.m.
Sunday 2 p.m. to 5 p.m. Closed Mondays

Galleries, opening times and tour dates subject to alteration

Myself

It's not fair

My name is Mark.
They make me go
Down the farm
In the dark
To get the eggs,
Milk and bread.
I wish I was brave
And not such a slave.
My torch is my
Only real friend.

Mark Riches (7)
Homefield V C First School,
Bradwell,
Great Yarmouth,
Norfolk

Innocence

I remember as a child,
How I used to carry my pot of gold.
Not the gold that you can buy,
But pure love,
Deep, sincere,
Tender.

I would take care,
Not to spill any,
Or waste any drops on cold hearts.

But now,
I have none left.
Just a dull aching throb.
Pain too deep for tears,
But just suffocating,
As if it would hurt if I breathed.

I was careless,
I tripped and spilt all my love,
On what I thought was a bed,
Of rose petals.
But it was only a floor,
Of cold, stone flags.
Which soaked up all my love,
Until the very last sweet murmur had gone,
And then,
It rejected me.

That bitter pain of rejection,
Crumpled my heart,
And left me broken.
Feeling cold, alone,
Desolate.

Janette Richardson (16)
Billericay School,
Billericay, Essex

Lost

Dread of wide, moist smiles
And expressionless faces.

A newspaper head with thinning hair
Clutches a black leather briefcase
To its knees.

Mother sang hymns on Sunday
Which drew tears
They itched their way
Down into my hair
Unseen, unheard they flow
Digging channels deep into my face.

My mind retreats to jagged heads
Whose cracked, sore edges
Were pushed back in
By warm, rubbing hands.

Rachel Ind (17)
Dursley, Glos
(Highly commended)

'With My Dog in the Garden', Heather Gear (12)

Untitled

And it seems that I have grown
Not so much cynical
As too analytical;
Too questioning; too near
To answers that will not satisfy.
I shall not love you:
I dare not love you.

One day I will lose you,
And in my sorrow send you poetry,
Proclaiming that this is love;
Lyrically bemoaning how a paradise was lost;
Claiming your affections
Off-set all my own confusions.
But I will be lying.
The itinerant minstrel,
Selfishly perpetrating
Both half-truths and untruths,
To satisfy his own remorseful conscience.
I tell you now,
I do not love you:
I dare not love you.

You will find me clumsy; careless;
More than a little absent-minded.
And what I tend to lose
Is what I tend to hold most dear to me.
Do not entrust me with anything precious.
I grow afraid to gamble
If the stakes should rise too high –
My hand cannot be that strong.
I do not love you,
Simply because I dare not love you.

Stephen Lee (17)
The Aelfgar Centre,
Rugeley, Staffs
(Highly commended)

Strange day

It's been a strange day.
Nothing much has happened,
Just a series of confused ideas,
Floating around in oblivion.
A cold, dark day, not only in the weather
But in a locked room in my very being.
A cold, dark day in this most beautiful of seasons,
For there is more beauty in the bleak than in the bright.

This is a day for being an island,
For locking out the world and its tedium.
If I stop and listen
I can hear hundreds of islands,
Passing down life's ocean,
Pondering on what a strange day it's been.

Geraldine Roberts (16)
Walton, Liverpool

Crusade

'Wasted potential' she said.
But I was happy with it,
in my unmade bed.
Fear alone was holding her now,
pushing first one foot then the other
towards You and Your ideals
that grip, and blinker, and smother
every part of her; stout shoes,
proud face, sad eyes.
She lives for an idea
and believes Your lies,
and in her own heroism.

But the real heroes are those
who stay in bed on Sundays,
and other wet mornings,
and can hear, and see, and laugh, and cry,
and live
and will one day die
utterly full and unbroken.

Rachel Cooke (16)
Sheffield, S. Yorks

Unknown alphabet

The guilt was there inside me
Lurking in the shade of misery
My words came out all twisted
A jumble of unknown alphabet
A wall was building up in my mind
Against this shadow and against the truth
The questioning in his eyes
Was one of torment and rage
I began to weaken under his power
My wall began to crack
And the tears leaked through.

Kerry Anderson (12)
Gosforth Central Middle School,
Newcastle upon Tyne

First day of the holidays

It's early.

My body is heavy and relaxed.
My tousled head, warm in the hollow of the pillow.
My eyes feel delightfully fresh and cool.

It's excitement.

A bubbling underground spring,
longing to burst free,
to express effervescently the undiscovered.

It's ecstasy.

Like the birth of a sneeze.
The sparkling crest of a yawn.
The calm, after spasms
of perpetual hiccups.

I stretch.
And throw wide my sunfilled curtains
of happiness.

Nikki Field (13)
Tunbridge Wells, Kent

Starting again

Sucking my thumb
   At one

Learning who's who
   At two

Eating my tea
   At three

Kicking the door
   At four

Really alive
   At five

Learning my tricks
   At six

Wanting to be eleven
   At seven

Thumping my mate
   At eight

Feeling my spine
   At nine

Starting again
   At ten!

Samantha Gidley (11)
St Philips C.E. Primary
School,
Salford, Lancs

Artist's impression

I painted my life on the canvas of time,
With my brush of emotion
And paint-pot of memories.
Each part had its colour,
Landscaped by the seasons.

In the spring lay the mint-green of freshness;
The silver of learning;
Yellow streaked laughter
And lemon tinged joy.

My summer was red.
It was scarlet with anger
And crimson with hate.

My autumn was calmer.
It held orange tinted kindness.
Its pinkness brought dreams,
Its falling goldness brought sadness.
My colours were fading.

Shades of grey made my winter,
Between black and the white:
Its blue was cold,
Loneliness lay in its violet shadow.

My portrait is ended,
My spring is beginning.

Ruth Elizabeth Eastham (15)
Fulwood, Preston

That moment!

The football went flying,
Through the air it went.
It was heading for the goal
Was it going to be a goal?
Was it? Was it?
It has clipped the post
And . . . .
Gone in, I've scored
Yes me, I've scored!
The winning goal, that's what I've scored!

Alex Sleightholme (10)
Bidborough C.E. Primary School,
Tunbridge Wells, Kent

'Under Pressure',
Philip Bentley (14)

Mud

I like mud
I like it on my clothes
I like it in my fingers
I like it on my toes.

Dirt's pretty ordinary
Dust's as dud
For a real good messup
I like mud.

Lisa Spong (9)
The Stokes School,
Blaby, Leicester

My hands

I have busy little hands,
They work all day,
Work, work, work they go all day.
I can tie my lace,
I can wash my face.
I can brush the floor,
I can close the door.
When I go to bed they get a rest.
I think that's what they like the best.
Thank you, God, for my hands.

David Moore (6)
St Eugent's Convent Infants' School,
Londonderry

Inside my body

I can hear his heart pumping,
And his bones creaking.
Listen I can hear his ear drums thumping,
Teeth grinding,
Blood swirling,
People chattering,
Lungs going in and out,
Loud burps,
Echoing sneezes,
People crunching,
Long snores,
Milk swirling,
Water gurgling,
Choking coughs,
Bones cracking,
Hair blowing,
Toe nails growing,
Feet stamping,
Hands crushing,
And soft soft soft breathing.

Ian White (9)
Buxlow Preparatory School,
Wembley, Middx

Funny folk

Wouldn't it be funny
If switches on my tummy
Could turn me on and off.
You'd know my brain was working
When you saw my headbulb flash.
You'd know when I was listening,
Because my ears would flap.
My eyes are red and square
From watching television.
My boots are large
My hands are small.
I am all wired up.

William Roscoe (7)
St John's C.E. School,
Dunkinfield, Tameside

My sailing bed

My bed is a boat, it floats along the water.
It goes up and down on the water bobbing as I
    dream.

Helen Louise Rowe (6)
Yatton, Bristol, Avon

Cough cough cough

Cough cough cough
Cough all day
Cough in the morning
Cough in the afternoon
Cough wherever I go
Even while I'm watching television
I – you know what – cough.

And I sneeze sometimes
But not very often.

Oliver Gray (6)
Bessacar, Doncaster, Yorks

Dream

Soaring above the treetops
Nearly above the sun
On a snow white horse I glide
A winged mare my steed
Leaping and bounding
Towards the west.
Over clouds in the heat of the sun
Floating through a great red sky
Faster than any earthly thing
Ever facing towards a rosy sunset.

Sarah Chan (7)
Barnet, Herts

The nightmare

I was enveloped in a swirling mist of red eyes.
Running blind with nowhere to hide.
Pursued by a host of beggars in jet black cloaks.
I was the hunted, the fox, running from the
   hounds.
And as I ran I fell, fell, towards a pit of writhing
   spitting snakes on the ground.
With long sharp fangs deadly to touch.
My pulse raced as I fell and I tried furtively to grasp
   a handhold on the sheer rock.
I woke.
My palms were sweaty and I felt dizzy.
Slowly I lapsed into a deep slumber.

Peter Richards (11)
St Martin's C.E. Middle School,
Epsom, Surrey

People

By magnolia touched

Look!
Look pal
At the man with the bright red cherry in his hand.

Let's let him keep it!

See, See –
See how he reacts –
Like a LITTLE boy
Like a SMALL child with
A new (shiny)
Green fish-net.

He won't cry yet-a-while.

He's married now; married he is,
With a four-offspring boast
Lining his fish-furrow.
He has a binge for rain,
            He likes it –
The rain. .

He's written a song, long,
And a Poem!
He's a running-person
With a strong frame, bent
To drive with.
He drives, he does.

In his chamber-home
He lives, he owns a
Painted Vase in a room of red-carpet,
Blushed-flush.

He worries little,
Says he's fine.
Fine says he.
Sings 'Tempus-fugit'
'Sleep-a-bit'
'Now-and-then' to rhyme,
To rhyme –
                    In a non-competitive
                    Turn-of-phrase.

He's got a name
– He's got two.
Painted his lodge,
His home-lodge with
Pretty petal-paint for a
Wife-to-be.
His real life-wife with a
Heart of charity and
Never-lies, in a bowl of love;
Pretty . . . and going cheap.

Lute-treated is he,
Sings a trendy Madelon to
His busy business.
He's no Dictator!
He's not lost!
Shalom's his god, under
His very own:
                    dark circle-spec's.

He blesses and is blessed;
With a little
(Just a little)
Pride and Prejudice.

His name!
His name is 'Jon'.
Jon, not John!

– He's no rock!
   He's no island!
   He's alright!

For now.

Timothy St John Troughton (17)
Holywood, Co. Down
(Highly commended)

The headscarf lady

There's a lady in our street
Who walks past our house
Every day.
She wears a blue and green headscarf
All the time.
Our neighbour says
It's the same headscarf
Since 1952!
34 years
In the same headscarf!
I'm always wondering
What's under it.
Has she got green hair
Or is she bald?
She walks mechanically
With her high heeled shoes
Clicking on the pavement.
She has a big chin
And piggy eyes
Peering out of the headscarf.
With her is a dog
Carrying a paper.
Is it the same dog
Since 1952?
She probably spends
The rest of her time
Hunched up watching the television
Or washing her headscarf
With the dog curled up
At her feet.

Matthew West (10)
Bushey Middle School,
Raynes Park, London

'The Queen Visiting
the
Royal Norfolk Show',
Rachel Groom (7)

Neighbours

We got a new car.
The neighbours got one too.

We painted the house.
The neighbours painted theirs.

We had an extension.
The neighbours had one too.

We moved house.
The neighbours moved
Next door!

Sarah Smith (13)
Col. Frank Seeley
Comprehensive School,
Calverton, Notts

Kitchenware

Leaning over the dust-bowl of this earth,
She is up to her elbows in filthy soap-suds.
Aside in some dish, filled with lying little cubed
    teardrops;
No reasons, no misery, a sheer vegetable accessory –
For the casserole tonight.
What tears? Just onions.
A sigh. Shrugging already hunched shoulders,
Her post at the aluminium sink is so wearying.
A husband to look after: no one remembers 'love'.
How . . . old-fashioned, devilmaycare, perhaps
Don't bother.
They're married; it's all complete.
So nothing else comes into it, no romantic
    flutterings
Or sweet honeyed moments.
Yes, some domesticated lifestyle of struggles
Crawls on with some uninvited slow ennui
Through the easy fantastic creations of rich
    daydreamers.
This is an earthenware mother,
With her soluble problems,
That dissolve in a cloud of bluey-whiteness,
With, of course,
More value for money.
So gullible.
So clean, so fresh, so simple: what a household
    cliché.
What tears?
Don't ask.

Yen-Yen Teh (15)
London
(Highly commended)

31

Whose confusion?

Nobody had the time to listen
So only you saw the raindrops glisten.
Nobody would see where the rainbow ended.
Or how the small folk could be befriended.
They never knew of the things you tried
When you said goblins had joined you
And you had tea in the garden.
They simply said you lied.
When the man in the moon played his fiddle
And you waltzed with a princess
To the tune of Hey Diddle Diddle
They just turned away, and
They never saw you and the unicorns play.
When you told of rides upon an eagle's back
They shouted at you until your head went
    SMACK.
They never ever saw
How the Mars men danced across your floor
Or how the giants brought you ice creams
As you sheltered beneath daffodils.
They never tried the witches' potions and pills
Nor did they sing with Harlequins
In their fancy dress frills.
When you tried to show them all the lovely colours
That really were like no others
They refused to see them, said they did not exist
So only you knew just what they had missed.
But they could not take the memories —
Of bathing with elves beneath the trees
Or searching for nectar with honeycomb bees.

They could never destroy your flights with the
     doves
Visiting far away lands.
Or how you brought statues to life
By the touch of your hands.
And even though they send you off to a strange
     grey room
And even though the windows have bars,
You can still get out and walk on the stars.
You can still have the excitement and whirr
As you parade your jewels and jackets of fur,
They pretend they can't see them –
Say you've lost your mind,
But you don't care
As the gobbledegooks are really quite kind.

Jenny Dowling (15)
St Paul's R.C. Girls' School,
Birmingham

The Mirror-man

Through looking-glass, shadowland,
Here comes the Mirror-man.
Mute lipped
Looking out.
Face and features cleverly twin,
But hide the Mirror-man within.
Wryly smile
Through your eyes.
The Mirror-man he knows your pain,
Secure beneath his silvered plane.
Lost soul
Chameleon.
The Mirror-man he sees
You see.
You live —
He breathes —
And later leaves you wondering,
If after all when you have gone,
The Mirror-man will still live on;
And live and see and breathe
And feel,
And whether he is really . . .

Real.

Andrew James Davice (16)
Sutton Coldfield, West Midlands

'Portrait', Bruce Bennett (16) (Award winner)

Fallen angels

'In sickness and in health,'
said the preacher to the pair,
as if sentencing them to a lifetime of care.

Baby bottles, pins and hungry little tears.
The preacher at the font plugs his throbbing ears.

Through fights, wars, and a kind of loyalty
they waited for their time,
when they would have no more papers to sign.

'Ashes to ashes, dust to dust,'
said the preacher to the wind.
They were angels once more – they had never sinned.

Carys Davies (14)
Kidwelly, Dyfed

Funny folk

His name is big ears,
And with his biscuit eyes,
There are tears of crumbs
Every time he cries.
His nose is a banana,
His mouth a rosy apple,
His hands are ten fat sausages
That he nibbles
For his dinner.

Gemma Richardson (6)
St John's C.E. School,
Dunkinfield, Tameside

Danger!

Slowly, stealthily, the man traces his steps on the
   girder,
The riveted joints all that he can hold on to.
His hobnail boots grip the edge,
His hands clasp the smooth steel of the girder.
With his flat cap placed firmly on his head,
And his riveting hammer and wrench placed firmly
   in his pocket,
His life on the line
As he treads cautiously along.

Andrew Robinson (12)
Ellen Wilkinson High School,
Ardwick, Manchester

The gymnast

The petite, tender figure,
elasticated into a slender shape,
performing the perfect balance,
not showing a tremble of fear.
Carefully holding an elegant move.
Smoothly landing delicately,
but with an elegant, positive action.
Gliding along, swooping gently along the beam,
creating a wonderful scene.

Lisa Montague (13)
Blessed George Napier School,
Banbury, Oxon

Windsurfer

As the windsurfer flies past
He grabs hold of the wet mast
As the turned head of the board
Curves up like a Turkish sword.
The windsurfer nearly capsizes –
All his friends are criticizers.

Ahmed Barud (12)
Ellen Wilkinson High School,
Ardwick, Manchester

The tightrope walk

The band starts playing,
It's time to go,
Onwards and upwards,
And on with the show.

The crowd goes quiet as I reach the rope,
And all they do is watch and hope,
Sixty metres above the sky,
Why I do it – I don't know why.

Left foot first, followed by right,
The rope starts swaying, the crowd gets a fright.
The crowd gasp and start to call,
As I fight for balance to save my fall.

I manage to hold it, the act's gone well,
Nobody injured, nobody fell,
I've reached the ground safely, I'm the star of
    the show,
The clowns come on next, that's the circus you
    know.

Phillip John Hoskin (11)
West Park Middle School,
Worthing, Sussex

'A Hand Stand', Selina Kirkley (4)

This woman will not change

Where factories, houses and shops are,
    Once there were fields.
The thundering, endless road outside her house
    Was once a meadow-sweet smelling lane.

She has lived through two wars,
    Has fought for King and Queen,
Has fought for country, and even harder for her
    children,
    In her woman way, among the powdered eggs
    and milk,
The saved teabags and the penny stretching
    pounds.
    And this woman will not change.

She changed with the times of her past.
    Ran on flamingo legs with the friends of her
    childhood.
Flirted and fluttered in the dances of her youth.
    Polished and cooked in the early days of her
    marriage.
Washed and fed her children,
    And changed with the days of her life.

She wept as she buried her husband,
    Then went on fighting.
Saw her children grow up, saw them married.
    Saw her grandchildren, counted her blessings.
And then saw herself, alone.
    She will not change now.

The world outside her house goes hurtling on its
   way.
And she sits and watches the shadows creeping off
   the wall.

She is silent, but she is not at peace.
   She understands, but she will not accept.
She will not fight, but she will not follow.
   This woman will change no more.
   This woman will not change.

Georgianne Griffiths (12)
The Red Maids' School,
Westbury-on-Trym, Bristol

Could you pass me the salt, please?

I saw a man on a bike,
                 panting.
He had no fingers
and only one thumb.

I looked at the trees.
How could he ride?
I don't know,
I didn't want to stare.

Later,
painfully,
he passed me the salt.
I just smiled.

Rachel Cooke (16)
Sheffield, S. Yorks

An old woman

She sits alone
in a small dark room,
playing back the faded reel
of her memory,
and watching long-dead friends
playing tennis
on the screen in her mind.

She spends the summer sun
rocking by her window,
listening to youthful voices
laughing outside her solitude.
A newspaper lies unread on her lap,
her eyes have long given up
trying to drill the unruly words
into orderly lines.

With tidy stiches
she knits her loneliness
into long scarves
for reluctant grandchildren.
There is no bitterness in her heart
when they do not arrive,
only a cloud of resignation
that smothers her spirit.

Shaheen Ashraf (16)
Walton-on-Thames, Surrey

The old man

He is sitting by the window
Watching children playing in the street.
They see him smiling as they play,
And stick out their tongues in disrespect.
They resent his aged presence,
His obsolete childhood repels them,
For a reason known only to them.
He seems antiquated – primitive –
His brain decayed with age.
He is an intruder in their game.
Laughing, they run away,
Robbing him of the simple pleasure
Of reliving his childhood.
Saddened, he hobbles towards the fire
To sit in his sagging armchair
Which is comfortable only to him.
It creaks, and then is still.
He falls asleep.

Lynn Margaret Dunlop (13)
Annan, Dumfriesshire

A Saturday night

He looks at his watch,
With a concerned frown.
He pulls up his neat tie-knot,
And wipes back his greased hair,
Sighing, he leans against a lamp-post.
It was late and she was late,
And they were not going to be there,
On time.

Nicholas Hornig (11)
North Bridge House School, London

The Stranger

The embroidered leather gloves
The turned up raincoat
The umbrella
The briefcase
The Stranger.

I peered through the window
Through the rain and mist,
A car drew up,
A black mercedes
With tinted windows,
I hid.

The chauffeur got out
And opened the door.
The Stranger got in
And they drove off into the night.

Verity Cobbledick (13)
The Red Maids' School,
Westbury on Trym, Bristol

'Face' Craig Mullholland (17) (Award winner)

Outcast

Alone,
All by himself,
He looks down at his shoes.
They blur, as some hot, angry tears trickle down his
    cheeks.
Why should he be left out?
Was he to blame that he was small?
Slowly he makes his way to the group of laughing boys.
They go silent when they see him.
He looks up at them,
But drops his head down to his shoes again.
He runs away behind the wall.
The laughing and giggling starts once again.
He cries.
He is an outcast.

Sara J. Rasmussen (11)
Aboyne Primary School, Aboyne,
Aberdeenshire,

Black sheep

The punk stands.
The clock strikes five.
The purge begins.

A cluster of carbon copy commuters
Spew out of their husty fusty offices
Into the scream of city traffic
And the obscurity of the crowded streets.

The purge grows,
As flocks of hustle bustle wives with
Screw tap heads turn to catch a breath,
And nag relentlessly about their brilliant children
And the awful sin of rising inflation.

The punk stands.
Head held high, hair still higher as
The people stop to stare and glare
And words like gas, mainly hot air,
Pour out of their half mast mouths.

'What on earth is becoming
Of youth today,' they say.
'They're so misled, their parents
Must be so irresponsible.'

But the punk still holds her head up high,
Not misled, she thinks,
Misinterpreted, perhaps, because
She knows that she is proud to be unique
For while they see one monster she sees one
    million sheep.

Elizabeth Lister (15)
Callington School,
Callington, Cornwall

'Mark York', Matthew Rowles (11) (Highly commended)

Alone

The house was shaken by a rising wind
that rattled window and door. He sat alone
in an upstairs room and heard these things.
Shafts of pale moonlight fell across the wooden
   floor
From a silent black night above.
They fell across his impassive features
and chased away the shadows of the house.

He thought of her and sighed,
a sigh that was echoed through the empty room
and out across the moonlit ocean.
Beyond the grey outline of mountains
lights of a far city sparkled against the sky
like iridescent stars on black velvet.
Yet the wind swept across the land
and through the leafless branches of trees
in its angry, solitary reply.
Slowly, hesitantly, he raised his eyes
which turned towards the open window.
Dark waves raced on to the empty sands
and through the silence of the night
a gull screamed.
He lifted his glass
and threw it against the blank, gaping wall.
Its fragments lay glittering on the wooden floor.
The wind subsided, the rain lessened.
The ocean became a stagnant pond.
Through the barrier of grey sky
the soft, oblique rays of dawn filtered.
And he sat alone in an upstairs room
and saw these things.

Sarah Margo Dunnigan (15)
Westbourne School for Girls,
Glasgow

Memories of a vegetable

Eighty-three years ago, he lay
In a white cradle, rocking, slowly.
Seventy-six years ago he blew out
Seven candles on a blue and white cake
With a little tin soldier
Standing to attention on top.
Sixty-nine years ago he turned fourteen,
His father died in the war.
His mother left home
In search of her lost love.
She too, was killed.
Sixty-two years ago he married.
Ten years late he divorced.
Another decade and he was middle-aged.
Thirty years ago, he met a
twenty-eight year old lady.
He asked her home and she slapped him
And walked out of his life.
Twenty years ago he went deaf,
Ten years ago he went blind.
Five years ago he was knocked down
By a car and paralysed.
He was put in a hospital
for the elderly and there he stayed.
Now he lies in a white bed.
Eighty-three years old.
A 'vegetable'.
But a vegetable with memories.

Claire Pearson (15)
Sidcot School, Winscombe,
Avon

Angel in waiting

Eyes stare vacantly
Surrounded by wizened lids.
Hair, withered wisps,
Skin a labyrinth of ruts,
Ears shrunk, deformed,
Figure stooped,
Wallowing in smothering clothes,
Frail skin pulled taut over rigid bones,
Flesh deflated.
Breathing restricted to gasps,
Haggard, conquered by age,
Resigned to death's coming.
But still there remains a girl,
A reflection of her childhood,
A wistful glance,
Or a feeble smile.

Ciarán O'Neill (11)
Cookstown, Co. Tyrone

'My Friend', Elizabeth Moore (6)

Conservative meditation

If I were rich by birth,
I'd be eccentric,
Cling to a teddy bear,
And hire the first chauffeur
Whose name was James.

If I were rich and a pop star,
I'd be notorious,
Be addicted to drugs,
And give my child
An embarrassing name.

If I worked in a factory,
I'd be a Marxist,
Join a trade union
And stage a sit-in
For more pay and fewer hours.

If I worked in an office,
I'd be Conservative,
Live in the suburbs,
And complain about
Increases in the rates.

As it is, I'll be me,
A hearty and sporting
Tory M.P.
A notorious chappie,
With an addiction for girls,
While happily campaigning
That 'Drugs are for Mugs!'

Gareth Bayley (13)
Hutchesons' Grammar School,
Glasgow

The drug addict

I am forgotten, lost in a dome of time.
If I break the glass I will melt away,
Dissolve and die.
A thick mist lies over my mind,
Metamorphosing into day-dream shapes.
Strange elations fill me.
Contours of life are unfamiliar and useless,
I have reached the last stretch.
As I painfully draw myself into a sitting position
Another day breaks.

Sarah-Jayne Toms (15)
Convent of Our Lady of Providence,
Alton, Hampshire

Norma-Jean

Blue eyes veiled in mascara and valium,
seeing nothing but screen credit takes.
Tears in a glass of gin and tonic,
that serve only to dilute the pain.

Scarlet lipstick smears a coffee cup,
or imprints memories on a stubbed out cigarette.
Peroxide glaze spilt on Gucci shoes,
and loneliness cast aside with a half-read script.

Mixed up mind locked in a cosseted body,
erasing happiness like blackboard and chalk.
A mask of make-up conceals the fear,
longing for that priceless freedom.

Billboards heralded this platinum goddess,
Norma-Jean Baker was her name.
Would she ask, I wonder, if she were alive,
for the price she paid to achieve fame:

Abigail Patton (15)
Friesland School,
Sandiacre, Notts

The Starer

The Starer stares at you
With his big staring eyes
And sniffs you out
Ready for his dinner
With his knife in his hand
Ears pricked up, listening for any movement
He rarely blinks.
His long hand all boney on the knife,
Staring all the time
His legs are still as rock
Waiting for the moment of triumph.

Helen Glover (12)
York

Violation

Avenue of foliage
With debris of morn
Hugged her as she leisured from school.
She felt in her pockets,
Cigarette end, lights to life,
Calming her from tutoring tension.

But within the walls of the leafy tunnel
Lurked the 'little girl dreamer',
The 'little girl exterminator'.
Like the owl in its trunk, out he looked,
But when looked upon,
Hidden owl becomes 'He'.

Female ears didn't twitch,
No breaking of twig.
She didn't even sense.
Why should she?

Girl . . . . .
Journey almost ended.
Man . . . . .
End of tether,
His mouth dry;
Like his stomach, his conscience growled.
Withdrawal symptoms crept in.

Bird of prey flew swiftly,
With whispering wings
And gliding ease.
Victim drawn to talons.
Vortex thoughts within girl's mind.
'Scream! Scream!'
But silent scream
Caused from the metacarpus clamp.

After he's finished, what does he do?
He leaves her,
Scarlet threads around her throat.
He can't afford to let her tell
For he enjoyed it
And he will enjoy it again.
For he is the germ;
The world is the breeder,
Spawning this bacteria
To infect the human race.

What can be done?
Unlike the owl, it will never be extinct,
A helix built upon a million others,
It can not be erased,
Quenched or destroyed.

Aston Hart (14)
Debenham High School,
Stowmarket, Suffolk
(Highly commended)

Other man's verdict

The sixty watt bulb only fuels my anger,
white-washed walls swim in front of my eyes.
Perspiration dampens my senses,
and coffee cups litter the table top.
Glancing through a haze of cigarette smoke,
I study the evidence,
what little time it affords.

Even though you are guilty,
you maintain a silence,
which only infuriates me more.
Do not think me so blind that I cannot see your soul
redden in shame.

Flat denials and calls for a lawyer,
irritate me.
Raised eyebrows question my authority,
but I am trapped in a starched uniform.
The colour of my jacket darker than your victim's
    bruises.

I have my arms tied by red tape,
my eyes blinded by liquid officialdom,
and my eyes deafened by bureaucratic bumble.
While you cower behind formidable ranks,
of solicitors and civil rights.

Give me the strength to resist temptation,
all I want to hear is your declaration of guilt;
sealed by the gavel's deathly kiss.

Abigail Patton (15)
Friesland School,
Sandiacre, Notts.

Home and Family

My home

Home, the place
  of all comforts,
The foundation
  of all ideas,
The birth
  of all opinions.

Home, the start
  of all arguments,
The end
  of all angry words,
The forming
  of all warmth.

Home, the beginning
  of a future,
The decision
  of a life,
Where the problems
  of growing up
  are told.

Zoe Whittington (13)
Elizabethan High School,
Retford, Notts

'My Grandma', Tracey Roland (6)

Summer holidays spent in my grandmother's town

The red stone wall
Near a railway siding,
Just too tall,
What was behind it?
Too young to climb,
I'll ask my grandmother.

There's this noise, like water,
Not fast, but flowing,
'What is it, Gran? Where does it go to?'
(The wall's too high for me to peep),
'I'll tell you tonight, dear
Before you fall off to sleep.

It's a secret elves' garden
With singing silver stream.
There's reindeer. And snowballs. And Father
    Christmas,
The sun always shines,
And it's always Saturday,
There's ice cream mountains,
And LOTS of toys—'
'An' can I go, Gran?'
'Yes, when you're a big boy.'

I dreamt for a year,
Wished for a year,
Grew a year taller,
But began to forget as I grew a year older:
New friends, new toys, new dreams.
Dim memory.

Lizard-leather feet
Bare on the scalding heat of an August pavement,
Fusing with workmen's discarded sand,
Lazily disturbing the dust of a lazy summer,
Skirting melting volcano patches of tarmac.

Lizard-leather feet
Ricocheting a tennis-ball against a red-brick wall.
Against THE brick-red wall.
That was no longer so tall.
There was this noise, like water,
Not fast, but flowing.
Scrambling fingers and feet
Gained the last few inches needed,
Until I sat and down could look,
Down into my 'secret garden' –
A dirty, filthy, stagnant brook.
Discarded broken prams,
Years of filth so old,
Generations of deprivation –
'It runs down beneath the houses, dear,'
I was later kindly told,
'It runs down beneath the houses
And meets a golden sea'–
Oh grandma, grandma, grandma dear,
Don't tell any more tales to me,
For tales are only used to disguise
The taste of a pudding that's burnt,
They're a topping cream
That's too soon eaten,
And everybody knows,
Eventually we wake from even the most beautiful
    dream.

Julian Christopher Aiken (16)
Droylsden, Manchester

Parents' sayings

My mum sometimes says:
'Shut your mouth and eat your dinner!'
Which I think is pretty impossible.
And sometimes she says:
'Do you know what a knife and fork are?'
Or, 'You drink that pop as if it's going out of fashion!'

If I climb a ladder to try and get my ball down
from the gutter, or if I'm sitting on a wall,
She shouts:
'If you fall off that and break both your legs don't come
    running to me!'
(As if I could do that.)

When it rains and I get ready to go out,
My dad says:
'You're not going out until you've done your
    homework!'
And I say: 'I've done it'. He says:
'You're still not going out!'
I just don't understand my parents sometimes.

Zoe Horsley (13)
Pudsey Grangefield School,
Pudsey, Leeds

I remember

I felt as though I had been hit by a wave,
I was so overcome with shock, that I just stood there.
Then I recovered.
The sadness nearly overcame me.
I looked at Mum,
And ran to her,
Like the sea going up a beach.
Mum comforted me,
By putting her hand on my head.

Guy Evans (11)
Dickleburgh Primary School
Diss, Norfolk

Water

On those dreary days in winter, how it tortured us
To run expectant to the table, but finding
Lifeless cabbage, sour swede and insipid turnips.
How we longed for summer and tomatoes,
Like warm, glowing fires filling the china plates,
To taste their sweet, ripe juice.

One day, late in spring, a great glass bowl,
Like an imposing general, stood sternly on the table.
No, I thought, it can't be, not in May!
But Mother dropped six tomatoes into the grand bowl,
And boiling water cascaded from the kettle,
Swiftly licking the skins from the scarlet fruit.

Bare-foot over the tiled floor skipped my sister.
She slipped, legs and arms splayed, grabbing for a hold
On the table, but striking the bowl with her fingers.
Shrill screams of agony resounded round the room,
Her skin, scorched and inflamed like the fiery fruit;
Steam rose from the razor-sharp crystals of glass.

Tears of pain were swallowed up in blood,
Seeping out from glass-cut skin
And mingling inactively in the steam, as if dying.
My sister suffered, unmoving on hands and knees,
As if in prayer for forgiveness,
Helpless and feeble under Mother's soft hands.

James McLaggan (13)
Dulwich College
Preparatory School,
Cranbrook, Kent
(Highly commended)

'My Father', Caroline Hopkins (6)

On a note of nostalgia

Sitting by his side
on a smaller chair
I used to wonder.
I used to stare vividly at the big, white
hands stretching effortlessly over the
oceans of the ivory sea
that lay beneath their palms.

Occasionally he'd turn his head;
a pair of ageless eyes would question me.
Yet I gave no reply.
For in a sense I was spellbound,
Bound by the spell of this music;
this recipe that only my ears could
sample.
The taste of these moments is long faded
and my father too has gone.
Yet the piano still stands where it's
always stood.

Samantha Newson (15)
Sidcot School, Winscombe,
Avon

In between

How's your father,
rolling in it,
I suppose?
Yes mum.
Smoking his cigarettes,
drinking his wine?
Yes mum.
Has he changed, does
he mention me?
Yes mum.
He looks after you well,
doesn't he?
Of course mum.
I do love him, you know
that, don't you?
Yes mum.
Do you think I'm
attractive, darling?
Yes mum.
Does your father have
any friends,
girlfriends?
A few.

Is she managing to look
after you well?

Yes dad.
In a way I still love your
mother.
Yes dad.
Your mother isn't taking
it too hard, is she?
Not really.
She is taking care of
herself, isn't she?
Yes dad.
Does she mention me at
all?
Yes dad.
She's a very attractive
lady.
Yes dad.
Oh, by the way, are you
alright?

Yes dad.

N. Smith (13)
Stoke Park School,
Coventry

'Dad's Workbench', Iain Sturrock (17) (Award winner)

Father is in – at last

Mother and child
Siting, on edge
Like an expectant father
Waiting, hoping.
The door bangs open,
Eyes are raised,
The door bangs shut.
A scampering from the child,
Shivering, shaking.
Smell from outside rushes in.

Suddenly the father,
Face neglected, breath damp with beer,
Comes in.
All eyes in his direction
He weighs up the situation,
In a calm voice says,
'Anything to eat?'
'In the kitchen,' is the reply.

The child runs to hide.
'Why ain't he in bed?'
Asks the father, temper brewing.
The child startled, looks in horror and in shock.
'He . . he was just going.'
Relief from the child
Knowing he has got out of the situation.
Mother, alone, afraid,
Father is in, at last.

Lee Whitehead (15)
Ellen Wilkinson High School,
Ardwick, Manchester

Animals Birds and Insects

Sunday psalm
Fox sleeps

Gulls hung in slung slums
Make an institute of noise as they lunge.
After the mist there is a hilt of smoke
From the lanes where goats sway on the hill's bend.

In the valley below the church chimes
                    and
Over the hills echo down the sleeves of silence.
In the queues of graves . . .
Awaiting absolution.

Fox dreams

And psalms web from the chimneys
Beyond the high hills in rimes.
A horn bays through the grey-gashed green
    awning . . .
Far away . . . and soft.
Quiver in the russet fur . . . *fox 'lerts*.
Sleep fled.
Slammed sun's shadow cuts the bracken.

2

Below in the valley's green awning
The dappled battle of the pack,
Tongues slung in the morning,
Wooing and whining . . .
Fox slaloms four legs slanting
This way now that, backward
Then back
Into the dead language of the catacombs . . .
Stunned gold fur streaming fetlocks . . .
Into the beckoning mausoleum
In the aftermath of benedictions.
Into the chancel . . . soft slink below the line
of polished pews . . .
And is gone from the grave place
Over the hills . . . long gone in that moment.

Hills arch, lurch . . .
Terror clung through their camber.
Through the hoof-hell hill of hounds and howls . . .
Pain-lunging fast-flowing fox . . .

And they spring now.

Sucked and spun lunging into the scattered
Scrum of the pack,
Ripping at her, running with her,

3

Pain slices in thin layer of nerve shriek
Unlocked in sanguine sections.
Dogs strobe the bloody bundle.

Woods whimper. Twilight flares –
An olive hood over the hue-hung hill
And a cadence of locked colours warps the sky.

Jesse Cabel Witcombe (14)
London
(Award winner)

'Canada Goose', Trevor Philips (9)

The hedgehog

At dead of dayfall the spiky rustler comes.
Stout and fussy, the pincushiony foodnapper
Darkles down ditches,
Grubbling gardenwards.
A midnight rifler through black bin bags,
The scurrying spinysnorter sniffles and scuffles,
Snailsearching.

Then, gutfully, he porkles back
Across the slugslimed street,
Till, fearstruck by a blinding roar,
He bristleballs.
And is splattened.

Why did the pricklepig cross the road?

Sara-Louise Holland (11)
Whittlesford, Cambs.
(Highly commended)

The otter

The grass was not moving
Yet I knew he was there.
He slid out, not moving a blade,
He is one with the grass.

He is one with the grass,
And one with the water,
For into the water he gracefully slid,
Yet not a ripple marked his entrance.

Not a ripple marked his entrance,
As he darted among the waving fronds,
A flicker of silver, flashes once,
Then weaves away.

Weaves away,
But too late is he,
For he has caught his eye,
Darting up he seizes his prey.

Darting up he seizes his prey.
That fish will not see the light
Of another day.
Out he crawls, his head held high.

Out he crawls, head held high,
Neck arched,
Fish in mouth,
He settles down to digest his prize.

He settles down to digest his prize,
Suddenly a twig gives warning!
He starts into the grass,
But it was not moving,

The grass was not moving.
Yet I knew he was there,
Slipping about, moving a blade,
He is one with the grass.

Ivan Huntington-Thresher (14)
Ramsden School for Boys,
Orpington, Kent

Fish class

From a bridge I look at the river
and my photo-copied reflection.
The fishes swimming round
like express trains
through the tunnels of
my nose.

Calling at –
South East Seaweed then
Central Anemone,
spot on time.
A streamlined fish class
service.

Then slowly the sun goes down.
Trains finish their journeys,
finding safe sleeping places,
shunting to the carriage shed
of colourful coral.
As my face fades.

P. Walton (12)
St Lawrence College,
Ramsgate, Kent
(Highly commended)

Frog

Frog basks on his lily pad,
Long legs dangling in the stagnant water;
A small green ball of mud
Gilded by the fading light of the sun.

Contentedly, he fills out his throat and
Croaks his presence;
In answer, a droning fly
Strays near to hand
And in an instant his
Long, whip-like tongue lashes out,
Rends the victim down from mid-flight
And conveys the morsel back
To his awaiting jaws,
Without the bat of an eye.
And yet, while he devours his prey,
A long, dark shape
Prowls unseen until
A thrust of the tail
Drives the pike up, to the light:
A flash of scales,
Gaping jaws revealing row
Upon row of razor-like teeth:
A splash ripples the pond,
A whirlpool skims across the surface,
And Frog is no more.

Rory Clarke (12)
Dulwich College Preparatory School,
Cranbrook, Kent

Frog

His smooth plastic skin pulled tightly round his
   body,
He sits by a moss-covered stone,
Watery eyes straining to see a single leaf.
Silent haze covers the pool.
Then a long thin tongue slices air.
Silk moth wings crumple and are engulfed,
And everything returns to hazy stillness.
A water skater jerks across the pool making dimples
   on a cling-film surface,
The frog leaps, then Sploosh!
And the frog is gone.

Peter Watts (12)
Halesworth Middle School,
Halesworth, Suffolk

The tortoise

It creaks along,
In need of oil,
From stone,
To creature.

The cogs grinding,
In the old fashioned motor.
Plodding patiently,
Head swaying,
Rhythmically with its body.

Its shell house
Bumping
Its old wrinkled skin,
As it drags its feet
Along its suroundings.

Samantha Blamey (11)
Darrick Wood School,
Orpington, Kent

My little gerbil

It's not like it used to be
Without my little friend
My little gerbil playmate
We'd play for hours on end.

He used to dash about his cage
Up the bars and down
And then he'd curl up in a ball
All fluffy warm and brown.

But now it's empty, cold and still
His cage a sorry sight
It's all so quiet and sad because,
My gerbil died last night.

Rachel Whaley (10)
St James C.E. Primary School,
Blackburn, Lancs

Cats

Spitting, clawing, hissing, pawing
with arching back
ears laid flat
crooked tail
a screaming wail
eyes flashing
claws thrashing
ears ripping
blood dripping

Squinting eye
slick and sly
tail curling
gentle purring
silent padding
cats cats' comfort seeking.

Anna Wilson (11)
Y Bontfaen Primary School,
Cowbridge, South Glamorgan

'Webster the Cat', Lucy Barnard (9) (Highly commended)

Cats

Cats are silky soft and sleek.
They curl supple round your
feet. . . .
'Time to go out, Fluff. Come, come out
of the door.'
The door goes bang,
the lock goes click,
time for hunting!
Once again savage killer
murderer
beast.
Suddenly a dog goes 'Woof'.
Fluff turns around
She curves her back,
and flashes her tail from side to
side,
she hisses and runs off into the
night.
She stops . . .
She hides and pounces!
She kills a bird! . . .
She has slit-like eyes in the
morning, as she waits at the step.
Mary opens the door,
'Why have you feathers in your
mouth' . . . she wonders.

Sara Budniak (7)
Yewdale Primary School,
Carlisle, Cumbria

Sheep

The sheep
Faces expressionless, huddle
Close to the wall,
That thread of black rock
Half obliterated by white.
The wind;
The icy cruel knife of death
Cuts deep.
A sheep's carcase
Lies,
Forgotten,
The empty eyes stare into infinity,
The fire of life
Extinguished.

Nicholas Perks (13)
Dalkeith, Midlothian

To make an elephant

To make an elephant
Take the dull, grey colour of the early-morning sky,
Six suits of medieval armour and the bark of a tree
For the elephant's hard, cracked skin.

To make the trunk, take a young, strong tree,
Beat it and pound it until it is soft.
Put inside the body the power of the sea
For the elephant's amazing strength.

Next, take a gentle, whispering wind
For the elephant's gentle, kind nature
And add to this a whirling tornado
To make the elephant's fury when it is aroused.

Find a bright, black jewel for the elephant's eye.
Cut two large, smooth stalactites from deep caves
Heat them and shape them into gentle curves
To make the elephant's ivory tusks.

For the elephant's huge, hard body
Take an enormous block of granite.
Chip it and smooth it until it is shaped
Like the elephant's massive form.

For its large, floppy ears
Take two National flags,
Dip them in a great dark stormcloud
Use sap from a tree to stick them to the head.

Emma Louise King (13)
Liversedge, W. Yorks

The wolf

Its eyes of amber
Its teeth of brilliant white
Its howl of the night

Its fur of silvery grey
Its paws as soft as snow
Its nose as black as coal

The wolf that wanders free
Over the plains of Russia
A silent shadow.

Nicola Hawkins (8)
Sunninghill School,
Dorchester, Dorset

The polar bear

The polar bear lives in the snow.
His fur is cream, not white you know.
He kills fish and also seals
Because he thinks they're good for meals.
He has his supper on the ice.
Silently he thinks it's nice.
He eats it quickly with delight
To fill his tummy for the night.
Quietly he goes to bed,
Curls right up and bends his head.
Soon he's sleeping in his hole
In the far-off lands of the North Pole.

Lindsay Robertson (7)
Newton Bluecoat School,
Preston

The wasp

The wasp,
A striped suit
Of tightly wrapped
Yellow and black pipecleaners,
With wiry legs
And bulging black eyes
Like coals from a winter fire.
He hovers malevolently,
His sting peevish
And buzzing monotonous.
He leaves a trail of commotion,
Shrieks and screams follow him.
The teacher stands, angry,
His lesson ruined
By this minute intruder.
Full of heroic intention,
I slam down my book violently
Like an eagle pouncing on her prey.
The buzzing subsides.
The wasp's brindled body becomes
Motionless,
With his thin legs
Dangling in the air
Like twisted, ruined
Pieces of wire.

Fiona Helen Struthers (12)
Uxbridge, Middx

The robin

A little robin in my garden
Comes each morning
To a branch
Where he sits and eats his breakfast
And then he does a little dance.

Rebecca Cordell (6)
Polam School,
Bedford

The bat

The moon appears and the bat
emerges from its daytime refuge.

He twitches his leathery wings
and in a flash he is airborne.

Fluttering, flapping, darting, dodging,
he is the master aviator of the moonlit skies.

With a click, click of his own Sonar
he detects a large moth.

And with a split second swoop,
his first meal of the night is caught.

Paul Hayward (13)
Billericay School,
Billericay, Essex

Flight

The golden sun sinks below the horizon.
It is night.
A silvery meteor streaks across the sky;
the birds are but the only ones to see its flight.
For the birds are but the only ones who can fly
     towards the stars,
fly with no feeling in their hearts but for the feel of
     the wind.
For the wheeling, soaring, curving feeling,
for the feeling of freedom, of being alive,
high above everyone, high above the clouds.
Swallows, darting and diving, flying swifter than
     arrows,
swifter than the eye can see, then plunging
     downwards,
capturing prey in mid flight.
Gannets, banking and soaring, then diving to the
     sea.
Proud, stately eagles, hovering on silent wings;
hovering, hovering till the moment comes
then plunging like a stone, deadly claws
     outstretched,
then swooping upwards, victim grasped in needle
     talons.

The slow, serene flight of the princely swan,
white wings rising and falling, whistling in the air.
The happy tumbling of playful rooks,
cawing as they wheel in jest.
In a flurry of wings the lapwing flies,
anxious to guard its nest.
The tiny hummingbird, jewel amongst its kind,
flutters its sparkling wings, hovering like a dragonfly
over some pollen-filled flower, always alert.
The herring gull soars high above the clouds,
gliding and wheeling on motionless wings.
A flock of starlings passes, no other bird surpasses
the perfection of unity this bird possesses.
Flying in their thousands, hundreds of thousands,
always together, never touching, swooping and
    banking,
diving and plunging, turning and tumbling, always
    perfect!
The joy of flight is in these creatures, the joy of the
    sky,
of the loneliness and emptiness, of the roar of the
    wind,
of the storm and of serenity.

Heidi Scott (12)
Ayr

Who killed the swan?

Who killed the swan?
'I,' said the weight,
'My poison lead she ate,
I killed the swan.'

Who left it there?
'I,' said the fisherman,
'When my day was done.
I left it there.'

Who saw her die?
'We,' said the reeds,
'She fell amongst our leaves.
We saw her die.'

Who will mourn her passing?
'I,' said the water,
'For she was my daughter.
I will mourn her passing.'

Edward Turnbull (14)
St David's Secondary School,
Acklam, Middlesbrough,
Cleveland

The kestrel

The moor is stripped of its brilliant daylight;
The shadows of the cultivated crop
Grow longer hour by hour.
Short, sharp, muscular strokes and the kestrel
   levels out.
Its mysterious dark brown feathered physique
   spirals on gentle eddies.
The feathers, cropped short, stand out like a
   crew-cut on a boy's head.
Far below, a whiskered fieldmouse ferrets for food,
Unaware of the danger high above.
The kestrel's bright, keen eye spots the movement;
Down, down it plummets; faster, faster,
Wind snapping at its golden head.
Snatch!
Its tiny form pulled higher and higher into the
   scowling evening sky.
That night only three mice returned to the nest
   under the sycamore tree.

David Griffiths (13)
Stockport, Cheshire

The eagle

The eagle is a stern bird,
Hunting all alone,
And as it glides,
We wondrously see,
Its marvellous beautiful flight.
Up in the air
The eagle flies,
Soaring in the lovely skies.

Sarah Chan (7)
Barnet, Herts

Ode to an owl

O stout gentleman,
Portly and proud in sunlight,
With wide eyes
Dozing while the lazy day flows by.
But with the night and the oncoming dark,
Are you transformed
To a grey shadow,
With a silent deadly face
Bloodthirsty, spirit of the woods?

Caroline Kershaw (13)
Midhurst Intermediate School,
Midhurst, W. Sussex

'Woody Who Visited the Library', Leo Nicholas Wood (6)

Chameleon

A myriad of flickering mosaics,
Kaleidoscopic on its corrugated
marble skin –
Scintilla in sunlight
but darkling in thunder.

Oh so changeable.

A play of colours, gleaming
joyful mercury,
Then exploding
with tessallations of
Violent sparks.

Yet still camouflaged.

Temporary tattoos on a
Masquerading harlequin
flinching reality
with iridescence.

All to be extinguished.

A tendril of treacle spiralling
from scaly jaws –
A quicksilver dart
Victimizing prey.

Tranquillized.

Independent, alien eyes.
Bi fold brain
to blindfold a knowing leer.

Beauty and beast are united
in a harmless,
prehistoric,
prototype.

Rebecca Brown (16)
Bitterne, Southampton

Racing the tide

With long tail flowing and dark coat glowing,
His eyes roll white in the bright moonlight.
His pounding hooves thump on the smooth sands,
He leaps a bush and with grace he lands.
He flicks his tail, then he twitches an ear,
He kicks up his hooves but he shows no fear.

His nostrils flare with excitement I share,
In the dark night, his mane gleams bright.
He gallops through waves, racing the tide,
Arching his neck, his head held with pride.
He enters a cave, his strides echo on,
I quickly pursue him, but he is gone!

Jennifer Digby (13)
The Alice Ottley School,
Upper Tything, Worcester

The last unicorn

When the last eagle flies
Over the last crumbling mountain,
And the last lion roars
At the last dusty fountain,
In the shadows of the forest,
Though she may be old and worn,
They will stare unbelieving at the
Last unicorn.

When the last sun is cast
Over the last starlost morning,
And the future is past,
Without even a last desperate warning.
When you look into,
The sky swept through,
And there she lives alone,
Hear the pain and the sadness of the
Last unicorn.

Rachel Oakes (11)
Histon Junior School,
Histon, Cambs

Strange playmates

You'd rarely see a Purdle
Or a Binkle-bonkle-boo.
You'd never find an Oom-pa-bump
In any famous Zoo.

You may find a Tin tan,
Or a Dinkle-Dee,
And you may find a Dum dul
A-chewing bumble bee.

And if you meet a Squinkle
This is what to do:
Wrap him in a blanket
And feed him Cockatoo.

If you find a Kelyock
And he is fast asleep
Give him to your Granny
As a special pet to keep.

So if you meet these creatures
Remember what I say,
For I know them all in person
And they often come to play!

Thomas Lynn (9)
Chelmsford, Essex

The Seasons and the Weather

Sunlight

Today, I have been tracing the sunlight
like an Inca, as it thickens then pales
through the day. Shapeless, it falls sharp and tight
across walls, soft on water, gleams off rails,

windscreens like a halo. I see it as
the true paradigm of clarity,
the air holding it like a crystal vase:
Delicate, and broken too easily.

Christopher Jones (17)
De Lisle R.C. School,
Loughborough
(Award winner)

Happy new (improved) year

Our previous model
(Cat. no. 1986)
Was so successful that
Cat. no. 1987,
New and improved, of course,
Is now available from
A supplier near you.

And eight out of ten owners
Say that
Our new, streamlined,
Compact, chrome-plated,
Infinitely BETTER
Cat. no. 1987,
Will enable us to
Struggle and fight
And surge on forward
In our frenzied search
For something whose
Name was lost with
The instruction manual,
With even more intensity
Than did the former, streamlined,
Compact, chrome-plated,
Infinitely BETTER
Cat. no. 1986.

Clare Connors (14)
Debenham High School,
Stowmarket, Suffolk

Daffodils

The daffodils
Wave in the wind.
God's pushing them.
The soft yellow petals,
Petals like silk.

Darren Jones (6)
Lodge Hill Infant's
School,
Caerleon, Gwent

'Red Flower', Sadie Thayne (11)

Here comes summer!

A curl of the hair
from the waving girls
a cascade of ringlets
dripping
      1
        2
          3
melting
ice creams
in the goldilocks sun
beams are thrown upon the sea.
A trick of clowns
on the slapstick beach.

Rebecca Heydon (10)
Cloudside Junior School,
Sandiacre, Nottingham

Snow in May

It is May,
And no one could have forecast
The sudden bleaching of fields,
Birches frozen against the half-light.
This has confused even the blackbirds,
Pondering in their nests;
And I,
Who yesterday
Lay in the sunshine,
Reach for my winter coat.
For once,
I thought that
I'd melted the ice.
But you are in conspiracy
With the sky,
And in this bleak land,
I cannot see the sun penetrating
The frosted grey,
Ever again.

Helen Wightman (16)
Basingstoke, Hants
(Highly commended)

Summer

The heat-haze hovers, humming
Over the bleached grass,
Crickets chirp busily among the grains.
A step is heard from far away,
Sandals slapping the age-worn stones,
Creating miniature dust-storms beside the bustling
    ants.
A lizard lazily lolls on
A scorched brown stone –
His eyes blink, and tongue flicks.
A plum drops, dark and ripe,
Followed by a broken leaf.

A dry straw hat lies
Carelessly upon the path –
A tired yellow ribbon flaps,
Fanned by a gentle breeze,
And the dry grass bends seriously to work.
The crickets rustle and sing, unseen,
While the world revolves.

Charlotte Davies (15)
Convent of Our Lady of Providence,
Alton, Hants

Harvest walk

Come with me.
Come for a walk.
The apple trees are bending.
They are telling me
That Harvest has come.
They are saying
That their fruit is ripe.
The fish are somersaulting
Out of the lake
To catch the flies.
The dragonflies fly
Around my head.
The corn in the cornfield
Sways in the breeze.

Craig Stovold (6)
Bedgrove County First
School,
Aylesbury, Bucks

Harvest poem

Fruit and nuts and berries,
Growing ripe and sweet,
Vegetables and golden corn
All for us to eat.

Rich food in its plenty,
Picked and stored away,
While others in their countries
Are starving every day.

Mothers in the market,
Choosing what to eat,
Perhaps a rich fruit pudding
For a special treat.

In heats of Ethiopia,
Little grows on land.
A mother looks at the food for the day
Which only fills one hand.

In lands of drought and hunger
No more, dear Lord, we pray
Will mothers ask the question
Which child to feed today?

James Anthony Carey (10)
Guiseley, Leeds

'Savoy Cabbage', Guy Taylor (17)

The autumn leaves

Crunchy leaves, scrunchy leaves,
Autumn leaves rustle,
Down the grey pavement
They hustle and bustle.
Swirling leaves, whirling leaves,
The wind is tossing,
They swoosh off the pavement
And on to the crossing.

Little leaves, brittle leaves,
Leaves wet and soggy.
The street now wakes up
To the morning so foggy.
Now damp leaves, now crumpled,
In the pouring rain.
Next autumn round
It all starts again.

Lucy Howard (7)
New Malden, Surrey

Autumn

A lovely day and birds flying and little flies and a
soft breeze, birds cawing, people walking and
talking and working and flowers opening, clothing
on lines, grass growing gently, going to school,
windows open, people in cars, the milk man
coming, leaves gently blowing, eggs arriving at
people's houses, people getting fresh air, people
wearing summer clothing, the sun blazing down,
people buying things, cats and dogs coming out to
play, people playing outside, people going out for
short holidays, the sun shining in your eyes,
clouds trying to look their prettiest, the sky
turquoise and light blue shadows glimmering,
October leaves falling, children chattering, builders
working, little trees growing, people having outside
barbecues, tractors working, farmers feeding their
animals, people going for small walks, people
moving houses, chimneys giving off smoke;
everything's peaceful and still once again.

Lori-An Darling (7)
Kirkoswald, Penrith, Cumbria

Day's end

Mellow, yellow, soft clear light,
Ushers in the coming night;
Shadows lengthen on the lawn;
The wreathing mist is upward borne
To mingle with its brothers brown;
And squirrels rustle in the hedge,
In search of nuts at forest's edge;
The lingering scents of bonfire smoke,
Thoughts of past Autumn days evoke;
And cottage doors stand open wide,
As homeward bound the children stride;
Stars gently peep from dusky sky;
The racing vehicles hurry by.
Upon the motorway each night,
The hint of frost is in the air,
A startled bird flies in despair,
In search of close embowering tree
Where, closely covered, it is free.
Now the light has died away.
Autumn night has come to stay.

Christopher Herbert (12)
Downsend School,
Leatherhead, Surrey

'Poppies', Claire Foley (10)

The dance of death

Autumn the great king has come,
His messenger, the wind, takes invitations to the
　　leaves.
'A dance, a dance, we are going to a dance,' they
　　whisper.
The leaves change into their beautiful ball gowns,
Goldens, yellows, rustic reds, and browns all
　　merge.
The leaves jump out of their old wooden chairs,
Out of their bare houses,
Down to a new world of a soft warm atmosphere,
White misty curtains,
Luxurious brown carpets.
The leaves whirl and twirl around the dance floor.
Winter comes and shoos them away.
They will not go, they stay and dance themselves to
　　death.

Heather Elizabeth Barnett (10)
Easterton, Devizes, Wilts

Changing of the year

Have you seen the killing of the leaves?
The dying leaves,
Descending to the ground.

Have you seen the going of the bird?
They fly away,
To the country that waits.

Have you seen the disappearing summer?
The light is fading away
In the far distance of the corners of the world.

Have you seen the plants that slowly die?
Their flowers that no longer exist,
The roots begin to rot away.

Have you seen the people wearing?
Woolly hats and scarves,
Getting prepared for winter.

Dawn Carrington (10)
Earith County Primary School,
Huntingdon, Cambs

Autumn

The foggy white mist
Drifts from the sky
The white geese
Fly to the South
The fresh smell of opening conkers
Fills the air
And the red rowan berries
Hang like beads on the trees

Victoria Green (8)
Brediland Primary School,
Paisley, Scotland

Autumn days

A chill in the air on a bleak autumnal day.
Haws, red, scarlet, ready for birds to pick.
Inky elderberries hanging in clusters,
While white clouds, like waves slowly whisk across the
sky.
Golden corn sparkling like treasure in a chest.
Animals ready to hibernate in cold Winter days.

Benjamin Bourne (7)
Corporation Road Junior School,
Darlington, Durham

The mystical day

As dawn fades, and the fingers of the morning
Spread chilled over the winter's hardness,
The eerie apparitions of clouds
Drift slowly – untouched they seem.
The strange effect of a fish's scales.
Then – the trees standing motionless, leafless,
Huge silhouetted skeletons towering above,
The sun behind them,
A king of white flame, blinding.
A ring, a glistening frosted ring casting light
    formations.
A solitary bird call – pitched clearly, distinctly
Over the empty expanse.
The ground, covered in a hard blanket,
Glinting occasionally.
This is a mystical day.

Emily Blacksell (11)
Fitzmaurice Primary School,
Bradford on Avon, Wilts

Jack Frost

Jack Frost painted
My car,
And my garden,
I tried to touch it,
But, it melted
Away.

Rhys Bennett (5)
Lodge Hill Infant
School,
Caerleon, Gwent

Search for Jack Frost

Shuffling and stumbling
I search for Jack Frost.
Berries are drops of blood
From the crystal daggers of ice.
Whispers die in the stillness.
A ghostly figure beckons.
Trees are shivering,
Haunted shadows moving,
Threatening, whispering,
Strangely rustling.
Lacy cobwebs sparkle
Leading me onwards,
Onwards into danger
Where spiky pointed fingers
Clutch at me roughly.
Distant sound of laughter.
Where are you, Jack Frost?

Heather Gardner (16)
Bedgrove County First School,
Aylesbury, Bucks

Ice

Ice is slippery, cold and hard,
Watery, spiky, smooth as lard,
Precious as diamonds, shines like gold,
Fun for the young but not for the old.

Ruth Salem (7)
Crossgates Primary School,
Rochdale, Lancs

Falling snow

Ghostly white snow, gently settling on a window
  sill.
Bare trees with hanging icicles from the boughs.
Rooftops suffocated by pure white snow.
Snow crystals tumbling to the frozen earth.
Snowflakes sparkle and glisten as they gently dance
  in the sunlight.
Snow under footsteps crunches like a packet of
  crisps.

Robert Coley (7)
Corporation Road Junior School,
Darlington, Durham

The beauty of snow

Cold this is,
Mute too.
Like an icy sort of fizz,
Falling down,
On me and you.
Wrap up warm,
It's coming down,
Disappearing at dawn,
No sound,
Eating up the ground.

Alexandra Nutting (7)
St Cedd's School,
Chelmsford, Essex

Snow

Ivory thistledown
Burnished with silver
Floating, floating.

Velvet frosted gossamer
Carpeting the world
Gently, gently.

A thick misty white veil
Visibility nil
Falling faster, faster.

Cottonwool cushions
Strewn on the motorways
Danger, danger.

Snow on the windscreen
Couldn't see that car
Panic, panic.

Snow-white cotton pillows
Snow-white linen sheets
For the dead to sleep.

A woman is crying, for
Not long ago she was
Marvelling at the beauty of snow
And now, it repels her.
She detests its pure whiteness
For it took away her son.

Ivory thistledown
Burnished with silver
Floating, floating.

Velvet frosted gossamer
Carpeting the graves
Where its victims sleep.

Lynn Margaret Dunlop (13)
Annan, Dumfriesshire

Snow

In the country
Still and silent
As smooth as velvet
With a strong taste of peppermint
Undisturbed.
While in towns
Its silent sleep is broken
By industry and human pleasure
And it lies
Muddy slushy beaten
And dead.

Juliet George (12)
Malpas, Cheshire

The snowman

There was once a snowman
In my garden,
'Mum and dad,
Come here,' I said.

He was moving
In my garden,
He threw a snowball
At my head.

I gave him
A bowl of soup.
'You look cold,
snowman,' I said.

He took the soup
In my garden,
He drank it, melted,
And fell down dead.

Stacey Walker (7)
Rufford Junior School,
Bulwell, Nottingham

A winter's walk

As we walk along the winter Downs,
The trees, bare of leaves
Stand like skeletons against the cold blue sky, and
reveal all.
Cradling abandoned nests and little else in their
windswept branches.

As we trudge along the forest paths,
Last summer's leaves lie trampled in the mud
Black treacle-coloured compost rotting gently in
every ditch,
While the last remains of January snow thaws in
dirty patches.

As we struggle with the clinging brambles,
We see trees showing new-born catkins, while
below
Brittle twigs snap underfoot and
Frills of velvet fungus spiral long-dead wood.

As we amble back in mud-caked wellies,
The mild winter sunshine warms our wind-chilled
faces,
Green shoots struggle through the frosty ground
A promise of summer in our winter's walk.

Sam Mountford (12)
Simonballe School,
Hertford, Herts

Winter

It is cold today,
On the window this morning is a pattern.
There's a puddle of glass in the street.
Your cheeks are red and glowing as if they are on
fire.
I shall warm my hands on your red cheeks.

Ernest Ogbonnaya (7)
Turnham Junior School,
Brockley, London
(Highly commended)

What is winter?

Winter is trees with snow sliding off their bare
boughs.

Winter is the patter of rain, and a soft, silent blanket
of snow.

Winter is pictures painted in ice on the window
panes.

Winter is hoping for a white Christmas.

Winter is cold, icy winds and freezing fingers and
toes.

Winter is Wellington boots and clearing the path of snow.

Winter is exams at school.

Winter is an army of shoppers, waiting for the January sales to start.

Winter is watching people trying to start their cars, and spraying anti-freeze on the windscreen.

Winter is sitting by a warm fire, eating toast and hot cocoa, wondering when Spring will begin.

Emma Louise King (13)
Liversedge, W. Yorks

Wintered land

Snow has fallen,
Bringing flamingo-pink skies,
Slate-grey clouds,
Parcelled children crying out in delight,
Scream and shout
Innocent of the frost air, nipping cold and wet melting snow.

Ashlie Munro (12)
Banff Academy,
Banffshire

Old man wind

Old Man Wind,
Why do you blow the trees to make them shiver?
Why do you whistle in the small gaps?
Why do you roar like a hundred dragons?
Why do you chase the gentle leaves?
Why do you push the small green grass?
Why do you pull my hair?
Go away
Until I want you
To fly my kite.

Mark Gardner (7)
Bedgrove County First School,
Aylesbury, Bucks

Haiku

Rainy day——
Wet glittering rain
glimmering on the window
shining on the glass.

Windy day——
Jumping racing leaves
Branches sway towards the clouds
Shiny wet playground.

Blodwen Strachan (7)
Bush Down C. of E. School,
Alton, Hants

Mist

grey mist
blocks everything in sight
it's like
walking into a grey storm.
the sun is
like a dull lamp up in the sky.
black blurs
fly through the air . . .
they are really birds.
trees are very dark patches
mist makes things dull.
I try to punch it
but I can never touch it.

Peter Curtis (7)
Bush Down C. of E.
Primary School,
Selborne, Alton, Hants

The night sky

The stars shimmer in the midnight sky. The clouds
 drift across the face of the moon. The silvery
 grey, crescent moon beams in the heavens. The
 owl glides down to catch his prey.

Kathleen Rice-Oxley (7)
Corporation Road Junior School,
Darlington, County Durham

125

Jewelled star-shapes hang
like glittering patterns from
silvery bushes

Philippa Threlfall (8)
Bush Down C. of E. School,
Alton, Hants

Night

The sun slips into its warm blanket,
As the moon rises from its bed.
The darkness is taking over.
The moon rises and the sun descends,
Like a see-saw in motion.
The sun's glowing, red face
Is replaced by a ghostly, white one.
Birds fly to roost.
Nocturnal creatures hunt their prey.
Lights flicker on in every home
As darkness descends.
The moon is guarded by
Millions of sparkling soldiers.
The streets, once busy and noisy,
Are now hushed and silent.
Dawn arrives.
The hustle and bustle of the day
Return once more.

Michelle Louise Friel (11)
St Andrews R.C. Primary School,
Falkirk

Going Places

Church

Peacefulness lingers in the air.
Soft footsteps of people,
Quiet voices.
Echoes of
Prayer
Praise
Worship
Trapped in the walls – caught in the arches.

Jasmine Threlfall (10)
Bush Down C.E. Primary School,
Alton, Hants.

The volcano

Once, on one fine summer's day,
A Dragon King rode low.
Over the China hills he flew,
Searching for his foe.
Yet later when the battle raged,
So weakened by blows was he,
That he fell from the China hills,
Into the azure sea.
    Now a million years have gone.
And we've never seen him fly,
Over the sunlit China hills,
Into the crimson sky.
Yet I know where to find him,
Only Time can set him free,
For he lies beneath a mountain,
That rose up from the sea.
    How peaceful and still a mountain,
All glistening, capped with white,
But it contains a Dragon King,
And he is filled with spite.
But wait! He's awaking!
Flee, flee, everyone!
For he is breathing golden fire
stolen from the sun.
Angry claws of liquid flame,
Tear the rocks asunder,
And through the heat and curling smoke,
Comes the Dragon Thunder.

Beware, for lakes of fiery tears,
Run down the mountainside.
Seep through the cracks, escaping,
To the burning world outside.
  Blackened spectres of the wind,
Issue from his breath,
And moan and swirl into the world,
Like messengers of Death.
But see! The Dragon King bursts forth,
And is to the Heavens risen,
And with a cry of victory, escapes from
Hell's own prison. . . .
  The white sails of the sampans glide
along the golden shores.
The slopes are green, the honeysuckles,
Kiss the breeze once more.
But men still fear the white-capped peaks,
To this day they still sing,
About the terrible revenge,
of China's Dragon King.

Claire Hajaj (11)
The Lady Eleanor Holles School,
Hampton, Middx

A gate

A green rusty
　　Gate swings
　　Gently in
　the biting
　　wind,
While an old
　lamp
　　stands
　rusting
　　motionless
　like a
　　bird cage.
The dustbin,
　grey and
　　spooky,
　like a
　　dungeon
　with rusting
　bars.

Victoria Douglas (7)
Lynsted and Norton
County Primary School
Nr Sittingbourne,
Kent

The wood

I walked between knobbly pillars of history,
Their twisted limbs bearing tribute to their age,
Silently watching, motionlessly observing,
Old and wise as any sage.
I trod where royalty had passed,
Chasing through the wild and russet bed,
I saw a fallow deer, as they had done,
And heard the squat oak shake its tangled head.
For nine hundred years this forest has been New,
For two hundred the oak and beech have stood,
And many have sought the peace of its glades,
And touched the archives treasured in the wood.

Georgina Ruffhead (15)
New Milton, Hants.

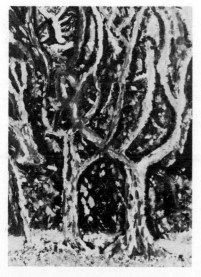

'Enchanted Woods',
Ryan Cooper (10)

Blackberry

Brutal stabbing deadly thorns.
Peeling velvet purple mint green stem.
Jagged tear drop curled leaves,
Barricading the succulent sugar sweet fruit,
Guarding the edible delicious blackberry.

Kevin Green (9)
St Andrew's Primary School,
North Weald, Epping, Essex

Memories
A holiday long ago

By the River Severn,
A horse with a pure white body and a speckled
    pink nose
Is drinking.
The river and the rocks,
Causing a combination of
Rapids and calm.
The sheep munching at the fresh grass,
And the Welsh birds
Flying overhead.
The raw wind
Sweeping on its descent
From the tall hill.

In the doorway of a shop
A small boy with black hair
Muttered strange Welsh words
As he bumped into me.

Joanne Grant (11)
Dickleburgh Primary School.
Dickleburgh, Nr Diss, Norfolk

North Wales

I saw a sunny, sunny smile,
Slip truant across a pair of lips —
It made my mind whip westwards
To where the sunlight frolicked,
Like the friends, among the waves of Wales.

I saw a sparkle in an eye,
Elusive as the mountain mist —
Where fun flowed as free, in me,
As the silver-white streams in
Waterfalls of Wales.

I saw the dreamy clouds, so close,
Thick as my ambitions above my head,
And wished that they were lower, to touch,
But knew that I must grow instead.

Graham Hill (17)
Billericay School,
Billericay, Essex

The moors

The moorland lay
Bleak and open,
Gouged and contoured by the
Ever unmerciful elements.
The stone walls and ancient buildings
Crowned the barest moor tops
Succumbing to nature's relentless revenge.
The dense scrub was buffeted by
Savage wind
But there still remained an
Untouched beauty –
The rustics and mauves and greens
Swept the slopes with colour.
The rivers and streams were
Cradled in the hollows;
The hill-tops were
Shrouded in webs of mist.
Everything passed in an
Endless time.

Samantha Clark (15)
Simonballe School,
Hertford, Herts

Ploughing

I hang on the gate
And watch
As a rabbit scampers over the furrows like a tear
Running down deep wrinkles in an old man's face.
Then a roar as the tractor rises
Over the hill,
Grime on the nuts and bolts.
The seagulls, hovering over the tractor like flies on a
Rotting carcass.
I look up, as the wind whistles,
Playing a tune in time with the
Seagulls' screams,
And I imagine a bird's eye view:
The fields and hedges, like a patch of corduroy
    sewn with green cotton.
And the furrows, like rusted corrugated iron
Surrounded by the ring of hedges,
Jesus' crown of
Thorns.

Rachel Ann Gardam (13)
Halesworth Middle School,
Halesworth, Suffolk

The seaside

Lying on a bed,
Sun hat on my head.
Seagulls flying,
Babies crying.
Sun lotion smelling,
Ice creams are selling.
The sun is beating,
My skin is heating.
Waves are crashing,
Castles are smashing.
Donkeys trotting,
Sea weed rotting.
What a perfect day!

Jackie Clark (13)
Billericay School,
Billericay, Essex

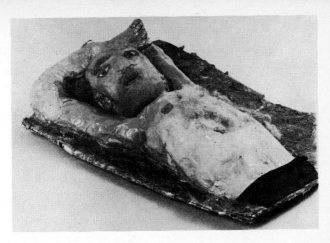

'Oh What a day', Leigh Morson (12) and Karen Burgess (13)

Reflections

A subterranean world stretching down
Into the murky depths of the river.
A distorted twin of Bradford
Floating in a watery world.
Down and down, a reflection of a house
Sinks to the bottom.
Red roofed houses rippling in the water,
An underwater world of darkness.
Under the packhorse bridge is another,
But moving with the breeze and current.
Houses swaying in the breeze.
Bradford's life and soul living in the water.

Mark McNeilly (10)
Fitzmaurice Primary School,
Bradford on Avon, Wilts

137

Upside down town

I know a place called
Upside down, a funny little magic town.
The pigs there bark
The puppies grunt
The folk wear jackets
Back to front.

The cows all fly
They're white and neat and
Birds go strolling down the street.
The sheep are pink and bounce around
And sing 'ding dong' as off they bound.

The cars and trains and buses too,
Are made of rubber soft and blue,
They travel slowly without noise
And don't harm little girls and boys.

I visit there whenever I can
I dream that I'm a magic man
With coat turned inside out bright red
When really I'm tucked up in bed.

Helen Anderson (8)
Thomlinson Junior School,
Wigton, Carlisle, Cumbria

The docks

An oily wave flops on to the beach,
Depositing more rubbish
To join the rotting, stinking heaps
Of unwanted refuse that huddle there.
The cranes that used to hold their heads high,
Cower uneasily beneath the leaden sky,
Their rusty joints screeching out in pain
With every gust of wind.
A hulk, more rust than paint,
Creaks mournfully with every wave which hits its side.
The quay, which used to bustle
With men, scurrying round like ants,
Has lost its workers
To the humiliation of the dole queue.
The gulls hover expectantly around a lone trawler,
Their cries echoing round an empty warehouse
That used to resound with raised voices.
Behind the cranes,
Graffiti-covered flats rise up,
Looking out over the desolate scene,
Across the silent sea,
To where a ferry steams away,
Its horn sounding,
Taunting the now-silent docks.
As the ship disappears into the mist like a phantom,
The only living beings are gulls,
Hovering like vultures,
Waiting for their victim to draw its last breath.

David Hilton (14)
Saddleworth Comprehensive School,
Saddleworth, Oldham

Lady of grace

Blanched, yet darkened periodically,
Illustrious, august, a nation's symbol.
Yet acidic air from city slums
Blows ominously across skyscrapers,
Damaging the legendary complexion.

The eyes are the window of the soul
And hers glow warmly.
Warding off and protecting as she stands
Astride the entrance to a metropolis
Created by man, blessed by angels.

She sees heaving city life.
Vice, turmoil, wailing sirens
Pierce the rippling
Of brown waters; pollution
Daring to wash at her divine feet.

Upon a forested, sacred peak,
Revered as a holy guardian
She should rightly be.
Not a meditating figure
For a sprawling haven of evil

Manhattan is no place,
For the Lady of the Torch.

Guy Jackson (16)
The Mountbatten School,
Romsey, Hants

Down the High Street

When Sunday has sapped
The life from the pavements,
Dorrington High Street
Stretches like a tired alley cat
Past disused chimneys
And windows where pungently flayed beds
Greet the world
Like the frozen half-blinks
Of empty shop fronts.
As paper bags breeze and spin
Around motionless drink cans
I walk the cracked and naked concrete,
Hearing exhaust pipes whistle and hum
Unknown poetry with the wind.
But only I am around to listen.

Andrew Wallace (17)
Orpington, Kent

Acceptance

Following the neon stutter
towards the city,
we lock our sights
on to the next bumper.

Ignoring the spawn of light
from distant streets.
Accepting the bulb's jerk
before darkness.

Sean Michael Ormsby (16)
Belfast

Little red car

Little red car
goes so slow
in the deep snow.
Little red car
goes so far
on a gallon of 4 star.
Little red car
brakes to a halt.
It was the silly boy's fault!
Little red car
moves on past.
Now it's travelling very fast.

Kirsty Buchanan (7)
Linlithgow Primary School,
Linlithgow

Intercity train

The intercity railway train
Comes dashing down the line again,
People talking, playing games,
Naughty children calling names,
A business-man with a serious face,
By his side a black briefcase,
Reading papers he scribbles words down,
Then looks at them with a serious frown.

Across the table a small girl sits,
And by her side her grandmother knits,
Down the aisle a little boy will run,
Pretending he's the driver, he'll have such fun.
A mother shouts,
Her baby cries,
The night draws on,
The time flies,
The train stops at the last of the stations,
People get off to meet relations,
In the morning the intercity train
Down the line will dash again.

Sarah Naylor (11)
Warrington, Cheshire

I wish I could go up to space

I wish I could go up to space
to see the stars so bright
and the big moon shining
but I am scared of heights.

Joanna McShane (7)
Ravenscraig Primary School,
Greenock

The man in the moon

I saw the man in the moon.
He was having his lunch.
He was eating star pie.
The stars in his tummy
Made him float around.

Elizabeth Halton (6)
Marston Green Infant School,
Birmingham

How to catch the moon

You could reach up
With a long stick
And knock it out of the sky.

You could bang your feet
Hard on the ground
To make an earthquake
And shake it out of the sky.

You could bribe a kangaroo
To jump up high
And snatch it out of the sky.

You could climb up Jack's beanstalk,
Throw a net over it
And pull it out of the sky.

You could put a rock on a seesaw
Jump on the other end
And catapult it out of the sky.

Or you could just leave it
Where it is!

Richard Hawkins (7)
Bedgrove County First School,
Aylesbury, Bucks

A balloon

A balloon goes up to the sky to see God.
It floats high above the clouds,
Its string following behind,
Whirling around and around.
'Hello,' says God.
'Hello,' says the balloon,
And it floats gently away.

Sarah Commons (5)
Headington, Oxford

Whenever

Whenever a dice
   rolls along
      the carpet
   it giggles
      silently.
Whenever
   a fish
      swims
   into
   an octopus's
   arms an
   ambush of
      sand appears.

Whenever a glue
pot is knocked
over a miniature
lake of
sticky glue
appears.
Whenever
a door opens
it creaks quietly.
Whenever the wind
blows through
the trees they
rustle.
Whenever a tidal
wave occurs
a boat sinks
like an
insect
drowning.
Whenever I finish
writing I always
think of an
ending
to wrap it all
up.

Victoria Douglas (7)
Lynsted and Norton
County Primary School,
Sittingbourne, Kent
(Highly commended)

Sensations and Feelings

Water

Slowly submerged in the cool, clear sea,
Grabbing at the board and hauling myself up,
The sun glistening on my watersoaked skin,
Small droplets hitting the water and rippling away
    to infinity.
Once up I must hold fast on the boom,
And pull it dripping from the sunlit waters,
The wind slowly gathers the sail, catches the gust
    and carries the surf forwards,
The fin slicing through the waters beneath my feet.
Then suddenly, falling I meet the swell,
Drops showering up into the sky, catching the sun,
Then falling once more to lie motionless in the
    crystal glazed sea.

Alison Knight (15)
St Gabriel's School,
Newbury, Berks

'Swimming', Katherine Gilson (7)

Have you ever heard the dew?

Have you ever heard the dew falling
Quietly,
Softly,
Lightly at dawn?
Persephone's flowers are washed awake,
And opening up
They lift their faces
        To the early morning sun.

The tiny droplets bedeck the blades of grass
Drenching the feet
Of Aurora's horses;
As they draw forth her chariot
        Bringing the dawn.

Jewelled cobwebs cloak the face
Of the spritely Faunus,
As he frolics through
The woods
And fields
Pouring his sweet music
        Out to the world.

As Helios rises
High into the lofty dome
Of the sky
He sets his bright sun to the task
Of drying the earth.
And,
Softly,
Quietly,
        The dew melts away.

Lucy Lovel (14)
St Gabriel's School,
Newbury, Berks

The river

River running, running westwards,
Cutting canyons to the sea

Me as I stand before you,
Not of aqua, but of land.
Exiled here on Terra Firma,
For I am trapped; I am man.

How I long to step from earth to water,
To be submerged in frigid green.
A myriad stream, a planet's life,
A taste of freedom, an impossible dream.

For once enclosed in liquid life,
I am death surrounded by the living.
A body to enter, as I entered yours,
A helpless victim, a life for the giving.

And so I climb, a sorry figure,
Clad in mud; clad in slime,
To shiver in air so essential to life,
And dream of how it should have been.

River running, running westwards,
Cutting canyons to the sea,
As you merge with saline greatness,
Will you still remember me?

David Connelly (17)
Long Eaton School,
Long Eaton, Notts

Childflit

When he tiptoed alone
Through sunlit lanes
And sung swayed
Child-flit games
In the shadow parabled barns
He daydreamt.

And even though the church sermons
Beckoned him in,
He turned away
To song to the streams
Where the ring of hushed benedictions
Slowly swayed.

O, childflood lullayed days,
The linked hours in love with the horses
Sky-dome-chimes
Through heavens behind clouds through his fingers
On the high hammocked hangar
In the mid-day aisles of sun.

So giddied by the gadding swing
He dives to the hay,
At love with life
And play and see
The rust of sky-flight filter with the breeze.

Time passes – fly the busy wrens
Ducking and diving through the dappled drones
    from the sky,
In love with the foxes
And still shy in front
Of the goats' tails and tongues
In the vein of summer
Runround like dragonfly – wings on the pond.

And the ganders
Gone from their pens –
long ago gone.
Then he climbs and falls
Gashed and rung, swung
And giddied by summer's swing
Sepulchral-shadowed sound
Echoing over the hanging hills . . .
Crepuscule.

And the swaying clocks free from time
Chime . . . incessantly
And autumn dives its leaves
And grieves summer's fainting sky
Time and time, time goes on.

And the lovers of the lakes entwined – and be gay
And linked hours
Mingled mimes
Make time play stay
Yet the clock still chimes
Their rhymes fold time.

Jesse Witcombe (14)
London
(Award winner)

Sounds

Some sounds are loud
And some sounds are low,
Some sounds are fast
And some sounds are slow,
Some are like lightning
And water that drowns
Or more like a pin
With hardly a sound.
Bells that ring,
And hurrying with a rush,
And then it's paper –
What a crush!
Mice that squeak
And noises at night
And spooky ghosts –
What a fright!
Or a sudden Boo –
Oh what a joke!
Or just behind you
A frightful poke.
Or a big black spider,
And then a bee.
If you don't think so,
Just you see!

Or then a car
Close or far,
Noisy trains
Zoom, zoom, zoom!
Or cleaning and washing
With a broom,
Or run along
Rush, rush, rush!
Or crunching leaves,
Crush, crush, crush!
Making cakes is much fun,
Or jogging
Run, run, run, run!
Or a spinning wheel
Just like cars,
Or a space rocket
Off to Mars.

James Martin (6)
Springdale First School,
Broadstone, Dorset

An empty house

Not a sound is there in this empty house,
Not a movement, not a whisper, not the squeak of
   a mouse.
There's nobody here — only me —
And I'm as quiet, as quiet, as quiet as can be.
And I'm not lonely — oh no, not me!

For forty years I have stood in the hall,
Births and deaths? I have seem them all!
Straight as a soldier, still as a rock . . .
Come wind me up . . . a grandfather clock.

Katherine Graves (10)
Maypole House School,
Alford, Lincs

Bubbles

Inside a bubble
Wet soft and smooth
A lot of bright light
The reflections of the sun
Quiet as quiet can be.
My breath blowing soft as air
A transparent light
Delicate bubble floating
Moving slowly
Twirling up
And floating gently
Down to the ground
Silent
No sound
Just a circle of water.

Andrew Walker (5)
Marston Green Infant School,
Birmingham

The china doll

How vain
The china doll
Stands in all her
Elegance.
Silk and satin,
Curly hair,
Perfect bows.
Such delicate
Airs.
What could spoil
Such perfection –
Except a fall.

Danielle Colclough
(11)
Bursley County
Primary School,
Bradwell,
Newcastle,
Staffs

Funny food

Engine oilade
Really home made.
Salt and pepper flan,
Made for a man.
Soil and worm stew,
Just for me and you.
Boiled slugs
and carpet rugs.
Baked peat,
For us to eat.
Sausage and snail pie,
With a tiger's eye.
Rabbit with slug sauce,
Served with dumplings, of course.
Fish and elephant grime,
Pond and pondweed slime.
Oranges and boiled shark,
Are better eaten when it's dark.

Alastair Warman (7)
Fleet, Hants

Tummies

Tummies go gurgle, tummies go splat,
Tummies feel sick when they eat too much fat.
Some are fat, some are thin,
Some are even pulled right in.

I can't think why God gave one to me.
It doesn't help when I'm on the sea,
But I do love it when I want my tea!
When I'm hungry my tummy grumbles
And I have to give him different crumbles.

Sameera Rangoon (7)
Fernhill Manor Junior School,
New Milton, Hants

'The Red Trolley', Jennifer Pritchard (15)

I would like to

I would like to write with my mind,
drink the fear of war,
paint the sounds of the moon,
video a dream,
dance in the fingers of fire,
see speed.

I would like to touch destruction,
paint interest,
write time changing,
talk to nothingness,
cut up sin,
see your life,
climb the sky,
feel a person's voice,
speak to time,
live under the oceans,
control the air,
take a cloud's silver lining,
see through the sun.

I would like to jump into a bomb and not be hurt,
crack the earth with my fist,
paint a heatwave's heat,
read a book that isn't there,
visit a drawing,
telephone a thought.

Matthew Peter Toghill (11)
West Park Middle School,
Worthing, Sussex

The sun rising

Busy old fool, unruly sun
Your presence awakes us
But not to rise,
It is a signal of life
And that which we
Together in love shall pursue.

Lust and desire
Perform our art
You should not watch
It is a private seduction.

The world spins in our bed.
Explosions of fire
Eruptions and chemical boilings,
Electrical transmissions
Pulsating fragments smattered about.

We rise to see the world in its full glory
And fall into an even greater peak.

Naked and free
Diffused,
Satisfied,
Wake us later!

Julie Louise Ashton (17)
Failsworth, Manchester

'The Angel Telling Mary About Baby Jesus', Claire Grace (5)

A state of mind?

Shafts of blesséd joy,
Pure golden thought,
Flowing, liquid, uplifting.
Its affluence fills every
Corner, crack and shelf.
It surges upwards,
Leaving you there . . .
Suspended and wonderful –
An unreasoned burst of bliss.

A thought jars – it all dissolves,
Leaving you shrunken, drained,
Only now aware of your surroundings
All is unchanged –
Yet so very different.

Katie-Louise Thomas (14)
Chelsfield, Kent

Heart – For Sale

Heart – For Sale
Several previous owners
Medium sized
A slave to love

Heart – For Sale
Mesmerized by love
Prone to be torn apart
Very efficient at sixty-five beats per minute

Heart – For Sale
Reliable ticker
Overworked in relationships
A field in which it specializes

Heart – For Sale
Several previous owners
Exclusive offer
A friend of Cupid
Apply within

John Meadows (14)
Billericay School,
Billericay, Essex

Warning

Dead end love
Going nowhere
Saying nothing
Just two people
Stoney cold and
Silent.

When I smile
And laugh
And touch
Your hand
It doesn't
Mean I
Love you.

Dead end love
Long time past now
Saying nothing
Walking hand in hand.

When you shine
And look
And take
Your toll
It doesn't
Mean you
Need me.

Dead end love
Drink the coffee
Saying nothing
You and me, dear,
Waiting for the
Bill.

When we kiss
Caress and
Hold each
Other
It doesn't
Mean
Forever.

Dead end love
Just a habit
Saying nothing
Counting passing hours.

Dead end lovers
Saying nothing.

Jason Rutter (17)
Ashton under Lyne Sixth
Form College,
Ashton under Lyne, Lancs
(Highly commended)

'Blobby Monster', Nicola McAllister (7) and Lucinda Scriven (7)

A tiff

I've never done a thing like that,
How dare you say I did,
I'd never take your brand new pen,
Then go and break the nib.

I've never done a thing like that,
I'm surprised you think I could.
I think you must apologize
I really think you should.

I've never done a thing like that,
I know what's wrong and right,
Go and make friends with someone else,
And keep out of my sight.

Frances Cook (10)
St Andrew's School,
Rochester, Kent

Learning and the Arts

Elegy

I found a glossy print of a picture
I recognized – a Corot work that shows
figures by a riverside. They gather
sticks, or walk leisurely along by rows

of sun brushed buildings on the opposing
bank. My Grandfather reproduced this scene,
recreating this world in his painting;
the tree's spread as vivid, the grass as green,

the water as reflective green and blue,
although one figure is missing, lost in
the grass. Fidelity to light, shape, hue,
makes it special, a richness that I begin

to appreciate now, with time; hanging
for all, although one figure is missing.

Christopher William Jones (17)
De Lisle R.C. School,
Loughbrough, Leics
(Award winner)

'Busker', Mark Gilbert (17) (Award winner)

All the world's a stage

Dormant they wait in the side-wings,
Actors, sycamore seeds alike,
Awaiting the golden spotlight
Awaiting the opening night.
Green buds; tentative
Creep on to their stage,
Slowly begins the performance
As befits their youthful age.
The tour advances with season
And with season the actors' skill
Ripens from bud to leaf-green
And then the most glorious,
True beauty arrives with the autumn scene:
Explosions of gold engulf the stage,
Autumn costumes, colour enlightens,
Trapped in the actors' cage,
And only unlocked when the leaves drop –
Colours fade with the final bow.
Their era is finished,
Spent is their glory,
Gone is their golden age,
Actors fall as leaves on stage,
Swept in the winds of the critics
Under the brush of a janitor's rage.

Julian Christopher Aiken (16)
Droylsden, Manchester

Folk dancing

I do dancing to the music.
I dream music
and I dance in bed.

David Winterfield (6)
Lodge Hill Infants' School,
Caerleon, Gwent

'New Wave Group' Merrywood Boys School
(Highly commended)

Legend play

A deer with wings
With a white
    figure
   pirouetting on
its smooth
    back.

'Puppet', Louise Kirk (16)

Gently
     the deer strokes,
silently
     the deer
     cares, lovingly
   for it's smiling
        fawn.
   A fox
curled up
     sleeps
     quietly
     on the
          hard
          wooden stage.
A handsome
     man skips
   from side to side
playing a musical
        guitar
     to a man
in a check diamond
        suit. It is
a scene from a
     legend play.

Victoria Douglas (7)
Lynsted and Norton
County Primary School,
Nr Sittingbourne, Kent

Not so impossible

You may think that this poem is impossible but if you put the commas in the right place after the noun in the middle of each sentence it will make sense.

I saw a fish playing the piano
I saw a musician eating pig swill
I saw a piglet painting a picture
I saw an artist eating some leaves
I saw a koala doing a handstand
I saw a gymnast with a zip up the middle
I saw a handbag climbing a ladder
I saw a window cleaner hanging from the ceiling
I saw a lampshade playing tennis
I saw a girl swimming in a bowl

I saw the man who saw this wonderful sight.

Melissa Bramley (11)
St Mary's Gate School,
Southbourne, Bournemouth, Dorset

The letter 'V'

Shaped like an arrow,
Point like a pin,
Wings like a jet plane,
Wild geese flying in.
'V' is a valley
Through mountains of green.
Upside-down on a boat
As a sail it is seen.
High in the air, it's the spire
Of a church
And the join of a branch
On a silver birch.
The tail of a comet, in space
It is hurled;
'V' is perspective, looking out
On the world.

Alison Coy (13)
Debenham High School,
Stowmarket, Suffolk

'S'

Like a snake
That sheds
Its scaly skin;
Like the sticky spring
Of Sellotape
Or spiral straws
That suck
Up squash.
Like slippery,
Sliding
Spaghetti,
'S' is two-headed
Like an eel;
Sweet yet
Spiteful.

Shots echo;
The fox's tail
Freezes
Like the winding trail
Of pursuers.
The final shot. Then
Silence,
The cold 'S'.
Silence breaks.
A swooping swallow calls.
Don't come down
To this cruel place.

Clouds shelter you
From reality;
Sky –
The peaceful 'S'.

Clare Smith (14)
Debenham High School,
Stowmarket, Suffolk

Hurries

At last

a word
'hurries'

hurries through my mind
to relieve me for a second
of the coarseness of vowel sounds.

'Umbrella' and 'soothing'
go arm in arm
with

'hurries'. 'Hurries' hurries
away. . . .

Oliver Nicholas Jones (17)
Amersham, Bucks

A parody on the 'Rhyme of the Ancient Mariner'

It is an ancient pensioner,
Was cooking in the shade.
By thy old tweed cap and pension book –
Do you make marmalade?

The bridegroom's doors are open wide,
'Marmalade?' quoth he.
The guests are met, the feast is set,
'Let's have a jar for tea.'

He holds him with his skinny hand,
'Ten oranges,' quoth he,
'With half a pound of sugar sweet
From Larousse Gastronomie.'

He holds him with his glittering eye –
The wedding guest stood yet.
'Boil it up and stir it well
And soon you'll have a set.'

The wedding guest sat on a chair,
He cannot choose but hear;
And thus spake on that ancient man,
The bright-eyed pensioner.

'Put lemon juice into the pan,
Put in the rind as well;
You light a match, turn on the gas
And make the mixture swell.'

The sun came up upon the left,
Out of the shade came he,
The pensioner shone bright and said:
'It's pure as pure can be,
No added artificial things,
And no E 123.'

The bride hath tripped into the hall,
Her costume tailor-made,
The pensioner looked hard at her,
'Does she like marmalade?'

The wedding guest, he beat his breast,
Yet he cannot choose but hear,
'I can't bear the stuff with all those bits,'
Quoth the bright-eyed pensioner.

Clare Murray (12)
Lady Eleanor Holles School,
Hampton,
Middx

The essay

My mouth twitching,
Slowly I parade the room,
Full of 2D, shifting uneasily
In their seats.

This is no test,
Just an ordinary lesson
With, of course, an essay.
One of my best, if I do say so myself –
The Adventures of blank the Snail.

Only one person in the
Whole room is writing.
The rest sit, chewing their pens,
Hoping for inspiration.

As I walk slowly round them
Killing all their imagination,
A small girl with a blue ribbon
Says to me, 'Sir, I'm not writing this.'
I pause, place myself in a
Position to tower over her
And begin, 'And why not. . . ?'

'I'm . . . I'm sorry, Sir,
But this is a
Load of Rubbish.'
She gets up to go.

'A detention, a detention,'
I shriek.
The whole class walks out.
I am left with
Half an essay and 31 titles.

The power of my word is gone.
The icicles at my
Fingertips have melted.

Ellen Jackson (13)
Henleaze, Bristol

Similes in the prep-room

I'm sitting in the prep-room.
Silence is about.
Until it's disturbed
By someone whispering,
Like wind rustling in the trees.
The whispering gets louder.
As if the wind's getting stronger.
As it rustles through the trees.

Suddenly, a smash and a ring,
A pencil-case falls off the desk,
Like someone playing the piano for the first time,
The master on duty comes in,
Like an earthquake and volcano
Happening at the same time.

Toby Longwill (10)
Dulwich College Preparatory School,
Cranbrook, Kent

Millimetre

Millimetre lives in a cube,
He carries all around the place, a tube,
He's a cone-shaped body and cuboid feet,
He never dresses very neat,
His spherical hands, his prismatic legs,
Are all the same, like round pegs.
His cylindrical ears, his rhombus eyes,
Are covered with circular custard pies.
He eats pentagonal peas for a treat,
But normally feeds on squashed shredded wheat.

Daniel Edmonds (10)
Dulwich College Preparatory School,
Cranbrook, Kent

Subjects: GCSE?

Maths is the unsolvable intertwining of numbers,
Unbalanced glaring equations,
Red xs and mental exhaustion,
Never achieving the infallible answer.

Biology is the study of agreeable green organisms,
An insight into the rope-like intestine,
A close surveillance of unsuspecting amoebae,
And forgetting how the earthworm respires.

French is learning what Marc will do tomorrow,
Accents carelessly flung on any 'e',
Saying stilted meaningless phrases,
Comprehending illogical grammar.

Geography is knowing the Amazon Forest's
    vegetation,
Giving detailed descriptions of effervescent geysers,
Putting as much colour as possible into a map,
And learning the Atlantic ocean is not where you
    thought it was.

History is analysing the past,
Probing into mysteries clouded over through time,
Finding out about Henry VIII's marital problems,
Evaluating information from biased secondary
    sources.

English gives leeway for creative freedom,
Endlessly answering questions on a well scanned
    passage,
Exploring the motives and desires of characters,
Aspiring to rank with the best competition.

Helen Catherine Oakley (14)
Rednal, Birmingham

'After School', Helena Wright (13) and Sarah Taylor (12)

A Cruel World

The archer's memories

Standing there with blood as cold as the sea,
Full of terror and dying determination,
It's your moment!
You pull back the string, aim. . . and fire.
Silence apart from the sound of the arrow whistling
    through the dark sky,
Shouts and cries fill the silence, but all you hear is a
    piercing scream.
You've hit . . . and killed,
You've *killed* someone,
You go boiling and then icy and all of a sudden you
    feel all weak and sick.
People cheer you but you're not sure, and as the
    people cheer you go and try again and again.

You now look at the historic ruins, and live it all in
    your bones again.
You tremble and think thoughtfully.
The memories haunt you like majestic lions.
It's all over . . . there is nothing you can do . . .
But remember.

Jennifer Mary Brown (10)
Langford, Nr Bristol, Avon

Dead in Libya

They found him
Under the rubble.

The Americans had thought it
A good idea
To bomb the city.
To stop the terrorists
They used the planes
From Lakenheath
'With British approval,
Of course'.
With whose approval?
None of us
Was asked.

But what about the little boy?
What had he done
Wrong?
It was not he
Who had sent the bomb,
So why
Was it his corpse there
Under the rubble?

Victoria Rudd (14)
Debenham High School,
Stowmarket, Suffolk

The silent drummer

Listen to the darkness on the silent battle field,
As the mist sweeps over bodies the lives of young
    men yield.
Listen to the drummer beating silently through mist,
Like the heart beats of a soldier who a maiden
    never kissed.

And, back upon the home front,
Will the young men never die,
Will their long tormented spirits
Find a resting place to lie?
There are people who believe
That war's a gallant place
And to die upon the battlefield
Is just another grace.
But, what they fail to realize,
What the people fail to see,
Is all the fear and anguish
In the days of misery.
Deafened by our arguments
What no one ever hears,
Is the silent drummer beating
Through centuries and years.

The snow of winter settles and it comes with
  freezing might,
Halting all the soldiers in their long and tiresome
  fight.
The soldiers all die silently in this war which seems
  so long,
Their tramping feet move slowly to form the
  drummer's final song.
Old men do not listen and few notice young men
  die,
But the drummer's haunting melody marks the
  place where
                    Soldiers lie.

Liz Ray (17)
Attenborough, Notts

'The Forgotten Grave', Claire Clifford (11)

Omaha beach

Nine thousand pure-white crosses
Stand silhouetted against
The lush green grass. Beauty obscures
The searing pain and futile loss of war.

Fiona Helen Struthers (12)
Uxbridge, Middx

The Button Man's song

I am the Button Man.
This is the Button Man's song.

Hunched here over computer console,
Nothing can caution me but my soul.
It is here I wait.
I watch;
I see.
The world outside holds nothing for me.

It is here I wait,
I listen;
I hear.
It is I who must wait for the order to appear

I am the Button Man.
With no political view
I press the button to destroy all of you.

I was the Button Man.
This was the Button Man's song.

Do not blame me 'cos the world is wrong.
I'm not sympathetic 'cos the world is gone.
I had my orders to obey.
I don't give a button that it ends this way.

Niall Dyer (14)
Debenham High School,
Stowmarket, Suffolk

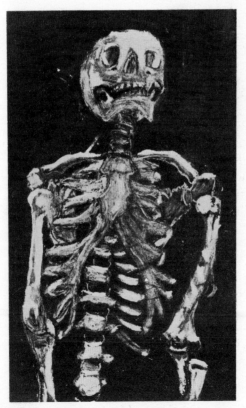

'Skeleton', Richard Morgan (10)

Nuke

Watch the sky.
I am coming from out of the shadow.

You will feel my flame, and laugh.
   I, who am Death, have come to you.
I will be swift, and there will be no pain.
   I am forged by your folly.
I come to cleanse.
   I, who am Death, shall ravage your fertile earth.
I come to purge,
   I, who am Death, shall destroy you.
I come to sterilize.
   I, who am Death, shall haunt your children.
Embrace me with a prayer.
   Do not forget me; I AM ARMAGEDDON.

Watch the sky . . .
And fear.

Sam Leith (12)
Downsend School,
Leatherhead, Surrey

The eyes of the world

Down in the city a child is crying,
Wrapped in a blanket, slowly dying,
A bridge its cover from wind and rain,
Crying for help again and again,
Unknown to the eyes of the world.

Across the bridge is a brightly lit house,
Full of joy and cries of laughter,
And a fir tree decked with coloured balls,
With tinsel and parcels galore,
Joy to the eyes of the world.

In a blazing desert far, far away
Lies a tiny broken-down hut,
Inside, a mother and six black children
Have one plate of rice for their meal,
Tears in the eyes of the world.

Above in the sky a plane's silvery speck
Is crammed with people, rich and content,
Who have not a glance, not a thought,
For those down below without food, without water,
Bitter to the eyes of the world.

Jane Stephens (11)
Westwood Junior School,
March, Cambs

Famine relief

Weary adults
Caress fly-eaten children
Ribs protruding through
Taut, barren skin.
A nation gutted
With a million dead
And a million to go
With skulls shrunken
And fingers, bones,
They scavenge, pray and cry out
For more, much more.

Ciarán O'Neill (11)
Cookstown, Co. Tyrone

Snap of the chain

These are the trees which fill the forests
All in the world that God made.

These are the trees which fill the forests
That form fossil fuel
All in the world that God made.

These are the trees which fill the forests
That form fossil fuel
That powers the boilers
All in the world that man made.

These are the trees which fill the forests
That form fossil fuel
That powers the boilers
That exude the fumes
All in the world that man made.

These are the trees which fill the forests
That form fossil fuel
That powers the boilers
That exude the fumes
That produce acid rain
All in the world that man made.

These are the trees which fill the forests
That form fossil fuel
That powers the boilers
That exude the fumes
That produce acid rain
That kills the forests
All in the world that God made.

Zoe Gleadhall (14)
Debenham High School,
Stowmarket, Suffolk

Inheritance

She, emaciated under the killing sun, cries alone.
He, chubby on the sun-kissed lawn, awards his
   parents with a dimpled smile.

The light of intelligence shines deep in her solemn
   eyes,
And she has already learned to care for her tiny
   brother,
While her mother . . . slowly dies.
He, carefree, with the tradition of a green England,
And cricket in a public school, struggles with his
   alphabet,
While his mother . . . proudly encourages.

She yearns for the exquisite drop of water,
Suckled from a solitary leaf,
But premature motherhood puts her brother first.
He splashes, swallows, swims and smiles,
In his frothy bath.
And screams indignantly when his baby sister tries
   to share his fun.

Hers is the inheritance of a sparse black waste,
Where water or lack of it
Is the only form of birth control.
His is the inheritance of strawberries and cream, in
   whites outside a pavillion,
Where water is a child's substitute for claret.

Her life is indefinite, precariously trusting in the
    compassion
Of those 'wiser' than herself.
His life will run its course, Eton, Oxford, MP, and
    Prime Minister perhaps,
And in his infinite wisdom, he will play with the
    lives of
Those such as her.

Charlotte Ansell (15)
Newbury, Berks

Islands

Unaffected by news
of distant islands.

Constantly shutting out
unrecognized views.

Until their realization
makes us effect our
own bloodless coups.

Sean Michael Ormsby
(16)
Belfast

Two stars

Two stars looked down upon the earth
as summer sun and light decreased.
The orb of rock each knew by heart;
while one surveyed the western part,
the other saw the east.

When one had watched this changing world
for many years, adrift in space,
it said, 'My friend, my side I've seen;
this curious world of blue and green,
how do you view the place?'

'I see a vast society,
whose wealth and income grow each year.
A way of life so civilized,
each secret every nation tries
to polish crystal clear.
It doesn't matter who you are,
there's food and instant home and school.
And everybody has their say,
and all the children have their way
while size and power rule.'

'That's strange,' the other star replied.
'If it is true what you have said,
why is it that the world I see
is hung with tears and poverty
and half the land is dead?
And autocratic leaders rule
the millions while they have their way.
Disease attacks and leaves no trace,
while every tribe or band or race
is dying day by day.'

The stars watched the earth spin away,
around the sun it turned and curved.
But still they stared and wondered at
the strange and secret ways of that
two faced, two sided world.

Andrew Lawson Campbell (16)
Newton Mearns, Glasgow
(Highly commended)

Time and History

The last visit

Ivory and incense
Sandalwood and satin . . .

We wander down dusty passages,
Years deserted
On the walls hang faded tapestries,
Dust saturated;
Mouse and moth nibbled;
Spider scuttled;
Cobweb spun.
From corners
And from behind cracking skirting boards
Come creaks, squeaks and
Pitter-patter of tiny claws.

Hands clasped,
Leaving twin footsteps in the dust,
We wander this English Pompeii,
Mounting stairs until we reach the nursery.
Here the floor is bare,
The old toys lie hidden in the locked chest in the
    corner,
Their children all grown up a long time ago.
Now the room reeks of nostalgia . . .

We climb more stairs to the attic
Relics of past lives and loves
Lying around
Weave our way through trunks, boxes
White shrouded furniture, once gone out of style,
And reach the small, curtainless, and dirty window.
We pull with all our strength
Until, creaking, and showering dust,
It jerks open.

Now we can look out over the shrubbery of
Dark and shiny leaved rhododendrons,
The frost hardened gravel paths
The sunken lawns
Where they lay lazy
Under white lace parasols,
All through the hot dry summers
All through those idyllic dog days . . .

But now winter has come:
The year is dead, and they are too
The house is to be restored as a 'stately home'
And summers to come will destroy its former
    privacy,
With their unfeeling, trampling hordes.

This house has three ages:
Today we see it in the middle age.
To the first we cannot go,
Yet to the third we dare not. . . .

Ruth Leader (16)
Westbourne School for Girls,
Glasgow
(Highly commended)

Echoes of a past

There is a feeling of closeness in that place,
    Of the past living on –
The feet of the present passing
    Where those of the past are still walking,
    Where grey shadows of the future
    Begin to form.
    And the past echoes
    In the leafless oak trees,
    By the strange crumbling fountains which still,
    In their death,
    Hint of water.
    And the unseen eyes of the watchful house
    Preserve your echo too
    For the feet of the future.
It is a place that knows, and remembers.
    Somewhere the boy in the picture will always be,
    Exactly as he was then,
    Still hugging his
    Stone lion.

(Written after visiting the ruins of Witley Court, and its adjoining church, which held an exhibition of pictures and photographs showing the history of the house. One in particular stuck in my memory – that of a boy, smiling, with his arm draped about a stone animal. He died a few years later in the First World War.)

Sarah Ratheram (15)
Harbourne, Birmingham
(Highly commended)

In the museum

When the explorers named the mountain,
And found on its slopes the unknown tribe,
This was history. And shouldn't history describe
Great events? Compelled by a still small voice
Telling them, 'Destiny hovers over this meeting',
Should the white men have fallen upon their
  knees?
Or should the natives have been shaken with
  wonder
As round the mountain-tops rolled the old gods'
  thunder?

But either the native was shrewd, bargaining
For copper, beads, top hats and pieces of cloth,
Or else the explorer, finding
In an insect's touch some nameless fever,
Stayed in his tent, clutched his gun;
Fingered his Bible, afraid to discover
A land where its writ would not run.
Unnoticed, change engulfed them both.

Now the gun and Bible are put on show
Safe in a remote, dimly-lit basement
Where, nowadays, few visitors like to go;
And though, in the museum, I pause a moment
Before this squat, expressionless grotesque,
Its face sharpened like a beak, no mouth or ears,
Arms like sticks hidden beneath its thick breasts,
I can see no god here.

Arnold Hunt (17)
Hendon, London
(Highly commended)

Lights out

Lights thin out. People grow small like flowers
turning inward to night, their worries shed,
like clothes, in sleep. Each floats over the hours
that seep deep and dark like an ocean bed,

to safe harbours of dream. I mark the tick
and tock, restless, awake: Thinking of those
who sleep at Pompeii; Taken by some quick
pall of fate, and left in hardened repose.

A place, people, culture holding its breath.
We mirror that stopped state now, a stasis,
where our own living is as still as death,
ambition, fear, desire meaningless.

Now, at Pompeii, casts seem to meditate
between life and death, with and without weight.

Christopher Jones (17)
De Lisle R.C. School, Loughbrough
(Award winner)

China dolls

Lifeless pale-faced dolls,
Colour faded with age.
Sun-drained Victorian clothes
Glassy eyes, some long lost
The dolls that stare are the dolls that scare.

They sit on dusty shelves,
Caged in with glass,
Cherry-red rose-bud lips
Innocent exhibits in museums and
Stately homes.
I see them come to life
Sinister horrors that haunt my dreams.

Keir Taylor (12)
Argoed High School,
Mold, Clwyd

Dorset as it was and is

Uncovering the layers
Of forgotten land,
Layers of life
Which once existed,
Looking back at the past.
Thinking of people
Who once lived.
Thinking,
Someday I will become
A thing of forgotten past.

Sindia Malhotra (12)
Cranford Community
School,
Cranford, Middx

Now and there, here and then

Perspective is clarity.

Showing the disparity
Between there and now
And here and then,
It has licence to distort
What purports to be the truth.

For then was there
And now is here.

Would that I had seen then
What I see now!
What would I now
Think of then?

Or rather,
If hindsight were foresight,
And I saw then
The things I recall now having seen,
Would the picture then focus
With any more clarity
Than the perspective now gained
Lights the disparity
Between what was to be
And what I feel now could have been —
There and then.

Clare Connors (14)
Debenham High School,
Stowmarket, Suffolk

Slowly

Slowly the parachutist glides down to earth,
Slowly the helicopter's rotors pick up speed,
Slowly the tiny acorn grows into the mighty oak,
Slowly the tortoise devours his dandelion leaves,
Slowly the dinosaur became extinct,
Slowly the year rolls round.

Robert Aley (9)
Westwood Junior School,
March, Cambs

Questions

Where is the end of the universe?
Infinity times past stars and moons.

How long is the future?
Longer than life yet shorter than domesday.

Why is a clock as it is?
It keeps time for the universe.

When does time run out?
When the stars collide, a second before.

How long does the morning last?
Until noon breaks.

Benjamin Regester (11)
West Park Middle School,
Worthing, Sussex

Attacking Missile Base Three

I ran across the long playground.
I jumped behind some stumpy logs.
ZAP! ZAP!
My lazer-blaster fired.
I ran past the crystallized being.
'Missile Bases One and Two destroyed,' my CB
　　crackled.
Twzap! ZAP!
I jumped over the ruins of Missile Base Two.
A loud explosion,
A big bang,
A shower of sparks.
I threw myself down.
BANG!!!
POW!
PLANG!
KOWPANG!
BANG!!
I was engulfed in flames.
I got up,
Brushed the bits of iron off myself,
'Mission completed,' I said.
Life-support-suit burnt,
I walked through the smoke,
Then had a rest.
Dead silence.
Missile Base Three blasterized.
'Three down and one to go,' cackled Ben on the
　　radio,
ZAP!
Another bogeyman I thought.

ZAP!
ZAP!
POW!
ZAP!
POW!
POW!
ZAP!
ARRRGGHH!!
Silence.
From the flames I approached it . . .
I threw down the pin,
I threw the rugger ball,
ORRING! the bell went.
I went into missile base
ULTIMATE.

James Parsons (9)
Dulwich College Preparatory School,
Cranbrook, Kent

The creation

In the beginning there was darkness in the air
The earth was nothing
There was nothing there.

So God decided to have a bit of fun
And created the planets
And the sun.

He decided to call one planet the Earth
And then this planet
Had its birth.

He made some darkness and some light.
He called light 'Day'
And called darkness 'Night'.

He separated water from land
It was all done
By God's own hand.

He decided to call the water 'Sea'.
'That is good,'
He said with glee.

He made the moon and all the stars
He named all planets
Like 'Venus' and 'Mars'.

He made the months and years and days
He made heat come
From the sun's rays.

And then the God Almighty, He
Created creatures
Of the sea.

And then made animals to roam
Across the Earth
Which was their home.

He made the grass and then the trees
And flowers with pollen
For hungry bees.

He then made people, Adam and Eve,
And with his help
They could achieve

Power over all living things
The fish with fins
The birds with wings.

Then on Sunday he had a rest
And that's the day
That I like best.

Alex D. Potterill (11)
North Cheam, Surrey

Pandora's box

Pandora had a box, a golden box with a key,
Pandora had a gift from the gods,
   but the queer thing is, you see,
Zeus didn't let her open it.
   She thought of all the pleasure
That she could have with what was inside,
   (She thought that it was treasure!)
She gave the key to her husband,
    Who really did adore her,
Oh, poor, poor, poor Pandora!

Pandora was inquisitive about the box of gold,
And because she was determined
  and as she was brave and bold,
She got up very early,
   and guess what she did?
Because she really wanted to lift that golden lid,
She stole the key from her husband,
    who really did adore her,
Oh, poor, poor, poor Pandora!

Her husband was still sleeping,
  so she tiptoed to the box,
She wanted to be silent or her husband would be
  cross.
And out came all the evil things
  that we still have, you and me,
Greediness and wickedness, bad moods and
  poverty.
'Close the box!' she heard, and trapping Hope,
   she made mankind the poorer,
Oh, poor, poor, poor Pandora!

Lucy Howard (7)
New Malden, Surrey
(Highly commended)

210

The Plagues of Egypt – a ballad

The Lord God said to Moses
'Go to Pharoah, go!
And tell that wicked ruler
To let my people go.
And though he will not listen
He will be made to see
That I am the mighty Lord God,
No other god's like me.'
But Moses was a shy man
And very slow of tongue;
Was very poor at speaking
From the time that he was young.
But not his brother Aaron,
For an orator was he:
God made him Moses' prophet
For to speak for him, you see.
And Aaron went to Pharaoh
With a stout stick in his hand,
Demanding that the Israelites
Be allowed to leave the land.
But Pharaoh's heart was hardened
And he did not let them go,
So Aaron threw his thorny stick
Upon the floor below.
And there before the royal eyes
It changed to serpent rare
And threatened him with mighty fangs
And penetrating glare.
Then Pharaoh called his sorcerers
To try and do the same
But though they all succeeded
Their efforts were in vain,

For Aaron's serpent ate them all
And triumphed for the Lord.
'Cos Pharaoh saw God's mighty power
And was truly overawed.

The Lord God said to Moses
'Tell Aaron, try again,
To ask that wicked Pharaoh
To release my Hebrew men;
And if he still refuses
To do my people good,
Then he shall pay the penalty
Of rivers turned to blood.'
And so it was accomplished
Just as the Lord had said,
And all the river creatures
Were drowned or else found dead.
And yet again brave Aaron
To Pharaoh boldly went
Threatening him with plagues of frogs
Unless he would consent.

And the river brought forth many frogs
To devastate the nation.
They made a nuisance of themselves
Beyond imagination.
Then Pharaoh said to Moses,
'Entreat the Lord for me
That He will take away these frogs
If I set your people free.'
So Moses went from Pharaoh
To converse with the Lord
Who promised that the frogs would go
If Pharaoh kept his word.

And so the frogs were banished
According to the Lord
But Pharaoh's heart was hardened
And he did not keep his word.

The Lord was very angry
At Pharaoh's cheating way
And summoned Aaron with his rod
To make old Pharaoh pay.
And Aaron smote the stricken land
Till it was plagued with lice,
And all the men, and all the beasts
Were cursed by Pharaoh's vice.
But still the people could not go
To worship in the land,
So God He sent out swarms of flies
Transmitted by His hand.
But still 'twas ineffectual
For Pharaoh still refused
To let the people worship
Till they were all confused.
To punish all the sinners
God sent a loathesome ill
Upon the sheep and cattle
According to his will.
But not on his good people
Did God the murrain send
Their cattle stayed alive and well
Until the plague did end.

But still old Pharaoh would not bend,
Or let the people go
To worship in the wilderness
As God had told them; so

The people next were plagued by boils
On body, neck and arm;
So very painful they became
It caused them much alarm.
And though his people suffered,
King Pharaoh did not care
He still refused the Hebrews
To travel anywhere . . . .

And now the Lord was furious
He sent down rain and hail,
The thunder rang along the ground
With fire mixed in its trail.
It damaged all the fertile land
And burnt down corn and hay,
But did not change old Pharaoh's mind
For still he made them stay.
In spite of Moses' pleading
He would not let them go,
So Moses, stretching out his hand
Brought down the locusts, so!
And every herb and flower,
And every tree that grew
The locusts they devoured them all
As o'er the land they flew.

But Pharaoh would not keep his word
To let the Hebrews go
So darkness came upon the earth
No speck of light did show.
For three long days the darkness lay
Upon the suffering land,
And none could work and none could play
And none could understand.

The lord said unto Moses,
'I bring but one plague more,
And all the firstborn in the land
Shall die — it is my law.'
And so the land was stricken
And all its firstborn dead,
But the Israelites lost nothing
For so the Lord had said.
And then old Pharaoh rose at last
To Moses said, in fear,
'Rise up, go forth to worship God
We want you no more here . . . .
Take all your cattle and your flocks
Your little children too,
Stay not in Egypt longer
We want no more of you.'

And so the people triumphed
By God's Almighty power
And left that wicked ruler
In that very selfsame hour.
They did not even stop to wait
Until their bread had risen
But took it in the baking trough
And carried it unleavened,
To Succoth, where they baked their loaves
And even to this day
'The feast of the unleavened bread'
Is kept a Holy day.

Nia Manning (16)
Aberystwyth, Dyfed

Cesar builds his canoe

Skills are being lost forever
    White men take the skills they've learnt
Need to pass on skills and knowledge
    So their parents seem not to die
What Cesar has taught his children
    Is to build a great canoe
This old tribe has food and water
    Making canoes with mind and hands
Making boats with the three trees
    Birch and larch and red cedar,
Birch tree bark for skin of boat
    A thin skin just like paper
Used for sailing on the river
    He is building night and day
Dressed in doe skin like their fathers
    Children strip the roots of larches
Cesar may be a great hunter
    But he's not too brave to sew
Sewn so skilfully with love
    Twisting tight round birch and willow
Red and resinous like magic
Steamed and gently rocked with care
    Take the cedar tough and strong
Bend the angle swift and sure
    Like a man with heart and pleasure
Makes his work with craftsmanship
    He rocks his body as he works
Sewing pictures with his love
    Carving Indians, dancing bears
Streaked with scarlet, blue and yellow

Cut the scenes of his forefathers
Remember them so they don't die
    Concentrating as he carves them
Steadily working by the lake
    Now the finished masterpiece
He can launch it as he smiles
    Children cheering as he launches
Cheering skills of centuries
    Cutting through the waves of Winter
Like an arrow through the air
    Full of forest mystery, magic
Between the trees against the sunlight
    Drifting calmly through the reeds
To the sounds of drums and dancing
    Sailing to the sounds of singing
This is Cesar's only treasure
    Treasured now and evermore!

Group poem by Class 3JH (9–10)
Hanham Abbots School,
Hanham, Bristol

The 1988 Cadbury's Poetry Competition

The Cadbury's Books of Children's Poetry contain about 200 selected entries from children of all ages and are illustrated with work from the National Exhibition of Children's Art.

If you would like to enter the 1988 competition whether in the Art, Craft or Poetry sections, you can write to this address for an entry form:

Cadbury's National Exhibition of Children's Art
Granby
Altrincham
Cheshire
WA14 5SZ

(Please enclose a stamped/addressed envelope)

Remember – you not only have a chance to feature in the *Cadbury's Sixth Book of Children's Poetry* but also to win a place on the Cadbury Italian Art Tour.

Index of titles

Index of authors